A DIVERSITY OF DRAGONS

Also by Anne McCaffrey

Dragonflight
Dragonquest
The White Dragon
Dragonsong
Dragonsinger: Harper of Pern
Dragondrums
Moreta: Dragonlady of Pern
Get off the Unicorn
The Ship Who Sang
Decision at Doona
Restoree
The Crystal Singer
Killashandra
Nerilka's Story and The Coelura
The Renegades of Pern
The Rowan
Pegasus in Flight
All the Weyrs of Pern
Damia

A DIVERSITY
OF DRAGONS

Anne McCaffrey

with Richard Woods

illustrated by John Howe

SIMON & SCHUSTER
A VIACOM COMPANY

First published in Great Britain by Simon & Schuster
An imprint of Simon & Schuster Ltd
A Viacom Company

Simon & Schuster
West Garden Place
Kendal Street
London W2 2AQ

Designed and produced by Bellew Publishing, London
Designer Ray Carpenter
Printed and bound in Hong Kong

A CIP catalogue record for this book is available
from the British Library.

ISBN 0–684–82112–5

CONTENTS

The Appetizer

'ARE YOU THE LADY who writes about dragons?' asked the male voice on the other end of my phone.

Warily I answered that I was. Warily, because, after the *Dragonriders of Pern* series became well known, I was apt to have some odd conversations with all sorts of folk. If the voice sounds young, I'm apt to inquire if mother knows he or she is phoning Ireland. With a voice of a patently mature male, there could be any one of a number of reasons for his query.

'Do you know a *lot* about dragons?'

That wasn't one of the usual questions I get asked but perhaps a variant on, 'were you fascinated by dragons as a child?' I am, however, reasonably certain – thanks to editors who send me books written about a huge diversity of dragons – that I have read most of the books written about *bona fide* dragons since the 1950s.

'I've read a lot on the subject,' I replied carefully. 'Why?' Taking the initiative might reduce telephonic sparring.

'I have a problem which I think deals with dragons.'

I instantly thought of Patricia Wrede's Princess Cimorene who volunteered to be a dragon's princess as she found life in the castle was so dull and boring, but this was a man. A Prince? Ireland doesn't produce princes, only clan chieftains and High Kings but not even an *Ard Rí** recently: even one with an educated Irish accent such as his.

'I can't explain on the phone,' he said, enunciating very clearly and softly to indicate the matter was far too confidential to be mentioned on Telecom Eireann and, perhaps, dangerous. 'I really need to talk to you about this dragon problem.'

'You're not a writer?'

'Writer?' He was both outraged and indignant. 'No, I told you, I've got to get some help and information, and I was told you were the authority. Please allow me to come talk to you.'

Male voices are not as good in projecting hysteria as women's but he sounded as close to that state as I've ever heard a man. From the rejection of my question about his profession, I felt reasonably safe that I wouldn't be asked to read *his* novel.

'Tonight?' His voice, which had a nice *timbre* to it, was definitely desperate.

As I had already seen that there was nothing interesting on the telly, I might as well find out what problem he was having with dragons.

So I gave him directions. My home is on a short hill above a major highway but you'd still have to find the right turn off. It's amazing how many librarians find it without directions.

To my surprise, he said to expect him at seven-thirty for he'd start as soon as he hung up. He had done so before I could ask his name or where he was coming from. That caused me some anxiety until I decided that first, he really was desperate and second, that such details were irrelevant to his urgent matter.

*High King (Gaelic)

When I told my daughter about my evening visitor, she gave her long-suffering sigh.

'I'd better *be* there, mom,' she said in her firmest no-nonsense tone of voice.

'Call me at eight . . .'

'He's Irish, isn't he? He *won't* be on time.'

'There's always a first . . .'

'Got to go. The boss's waving.'

Trying to get a handle on why this man was so anxious to speak to an authority on 'dragons', I reviewed our telephone conversation. In Ireland I could think of lots of reasons to consult authorities about other strange legends, myths and encounters. But not dragons. Immediately my favourite eccentric, whose name was Epiphanius Tighe, came to mind: he does that to you. Eppy is a cross between Yoda and Barry Fitzgerald with hair like Christopher Lloyd in his *Back To The Future* manifestation. Rumour had it that Eppy had originally been a Jesuit, but I'd never asked. He lives in a kind of cottage, half dug into a hillside in the Devil's Glen, and he has encyclopaedic information about all sorts of esoteric and eclectic matters. I did ask if he had an eidetic memory at which point he had put his index finger along his nose and winked.

He doesn't always give you an answer to the direct questions, but leading ones? You might be sorry you asked, for you'd get the answers to the last paragraph and period. He should have

been a professional *Seannachie**. But he had never turned me away when I knocked on his door to ask my latest leading question. No more than I turned him away when he knocked on mine: usually very hungry.

If there were Irish dragons, he'd know about them.

Generally speaking, Irish folk-tales went in a totally different direction: manly arts and head-hunting and warrior achievements and gods of rivers and castles under the hill and the Fairy Folk. There were more pigs, chariot races and stolen cattle than unicorns, dragons and hoards. But Messer Tighe would know if I couldn't answer this fellow. Of course, I'd have to go up there as Eppy is not on the phone. Though his place was crammed with all sorts of oddities, it was astonishingly neat. He could apparently put his hand on anything he wanted without much searching. Things seemed to 'come' to his hand quite easily. I wished I could say the same about my own office and library shelves. His ability to find the requisite volume in my library
was nothing short of magical: even books I didn't know I had.

I made myself finish the day's stint at the keyboard, ate supper watching the news, all well before the appointed hour. But as the digital moved from nineteen twenty-nine to nineteen-thirty, my Dobermann, Saffron, was roused from the couch and went to the door just as a red and black Pajero rolled across the gravel in front of the house and came to a stop. Saffie started to bark as a tallish man, dressed in cords, shirt and a blue, oiled-cotton hunting jacket with a cloth tweed cap shadowing his face, stepped down. He couldn't miss seeing Saffie in the big window, fangs exposed, barking her head off but he did not hesitate on his way to the house.

I grabbed Saffie's choke collar in one hand, slid back the door, told him to go right into the family room and take a seat at the big table. I felt informality might put him at his ease. Jamming his cap in his pocket, he obeyed and then I let Saffie go.

'She'll want a good sniff but if you're allowed to sit, she'll behave . . .' Hanging in the air was my usual threat, 'if you don't . . .'

He grinned up at me, offering a hand which Saffie sniffed before I called her away.

'I forgot to give you my name . . .'

'You were obviously in a hurry and you're dead on time . . .'

His grin went wider. 'Not an Irish trait, is it? But I'm not sure how much time I've got.'

'Oh?'

'Call me Sean. Sean Evans.'

'Evans' is almost as common a name in Wicklow as Byrne but I raised an eyebrow at him. He grinned, tacitly admitting that his name was *neither* Sean nor Evans.

'Now, what did you need to know about dragons?' I asked.

He gave me a long look, obviously debating if he could trust me. 'They don't *all* flame villages, eat maidens and devour knights, do they?'

'Good heavens, no,' I said, dismissing such limited occupations

*Seannachie Brendan, a Storyteller (Gaelic)

and bad habits. 'Depending on circumstances and species, mainly circumstances, they can be quite friendly, dependable, responsible . . .' Well, I may be biased toward Pernese dragons – since I invented them – but other authors have had distinctly charitable views of dragonkind, too.

I nearly jumped when I heard the doorbell ring. He certainly did. But, peering out my window at the front door, I saw the unmistakable figure of Epiphanius Tighe and his disreputable 125cc Honda which he was propping up cautiously against the front wall. He balanced his battered old helmet carefully on the seat: it looked like an American football helmet – the lettering on it might once have read 'Notre Dame' – and there was no face guard. Certainly it was headgear unlikely to have been approved by the British Standards for use on motor bikes.

'Don't worry,' I said smilingly to reduce the sudden frown on Evans' face. 'Epiphanius has a real talent for turning up at propitious moments. You've two experts for the price of one.' He looked even more apprehensive. 'Figuratively speaking, of course. I won't give you away but he's really as good a person on ancient dragons as I am on modern manifestations.'

I went to the door to see what else might have brought Eppy at such a serendipitous time.

'Just the man, Eppy,' I said genially. 'Come in. I've been wondering when I'd get a chance to browbeat some information out of you,' I went on in a voice pitched for Sean to hear.

'And what might that be, m'dear?' he replied, perky as ever with the twinkle in his eyes telling me that he already knew he was needed. How, I'll never fathom.

'Dragons. I'm . . . ah . . . I've been asked to do an article on dragons through the centuries and you know my limitations.'

'Indeed, I do, m'dear,' he responded, grinning broadly. 'But you've a guest.'

'Him,' and I dismissed Sean Evans. 'Your arrival is more critical and I doubt he'll mind listening. This won't take long.'

Famous last words.

'I've some stew in the pot, Eppy . . .'

'A grand lass you are . . .' Messer Tighe never arrived here well fed.

So, after I introduced the two, I asked Sean what he'd like to drink, and provided beers for both men.

'It's dragons you need, m'dear?' Eppy said after taking a long pull of the beer.

'Yes, you wouldn't have a few well-chosen words on that subject, would you? I mean the ancient ones. I need background on the breed.' The family room is part of the large kitchen in my house so handily, I could cook while entertaining guests. 'It won't take me a minute to heat the stew.'

From the way Eppy watched my preparations, I knew that hunger had at least been one of the promptings of this visit.

'So,' and he cocked his head at me, 'what about dragons?'

9

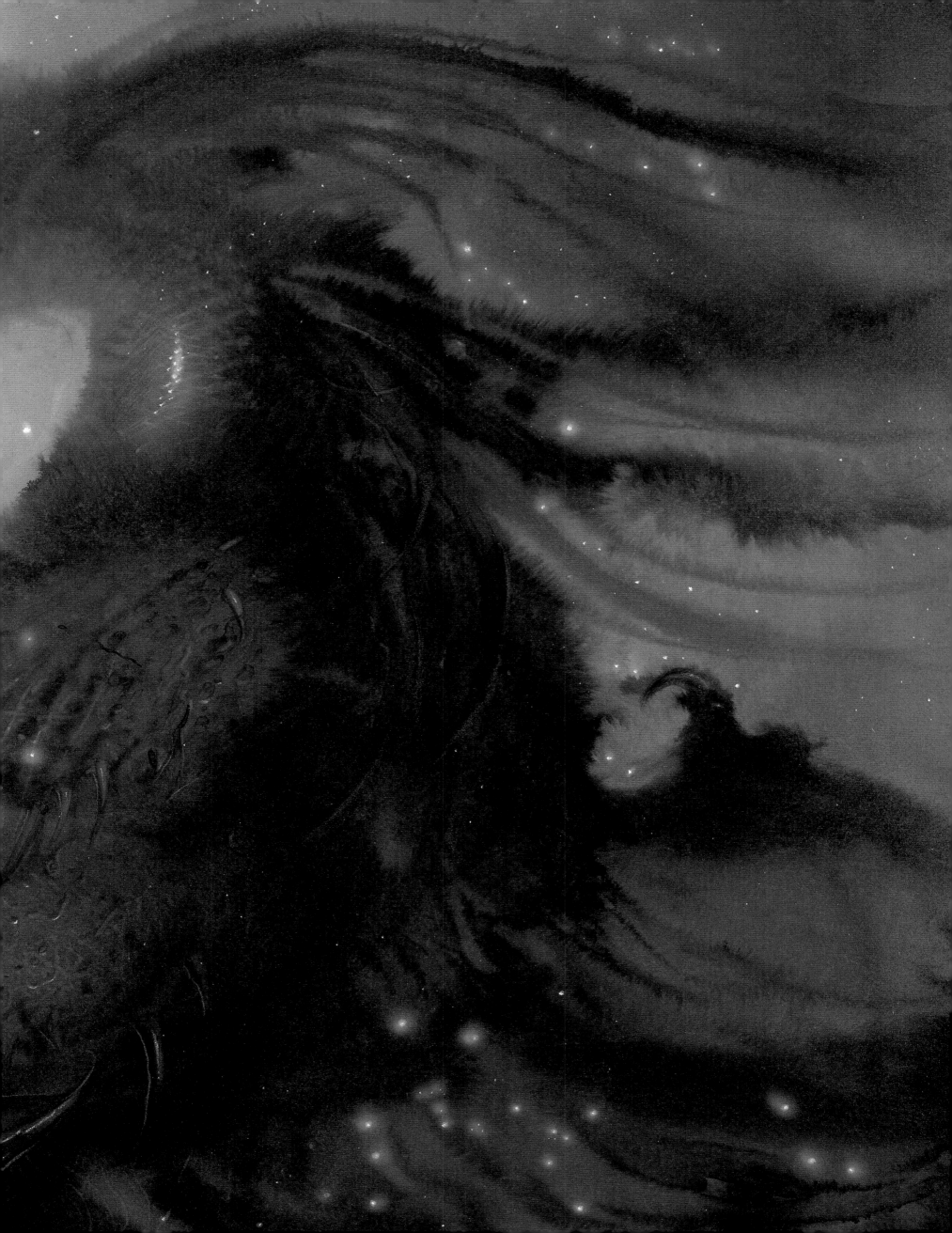

'*Are* there any in Irish legends?'

'Ah, now,' and he laid his arthritically gnarled finger against his nose, 'that's a very good question.'

Sean was pretending only polite interest.

'There are not many proper Irish dragons, that's true,' he said, wrinkling up his ample brow. 'But there *are* some. You'll find pictures in the Book of Kells, and St. Columkille was the first, you know, to describe the Loch Ness Monster. But that's not where it starts, not at all.'

He sipped his beer and then fixed each of us with a mischievous glance. Eppy, I realized, was about to unwind a ball of yarn.

'The dragon was there in the beginning,' and his voice had deepened and turned so unexpectedly sonorous that Sean regarded him with raised eyebrows and considerably more respect. 'Before stars or planets, earth, humans, or animals came to be, the great dragon ploughed the waters of primordial chaos. And the hero-god, by whatever name he was known, pursued and slew the wily serpent. Then, from her body, he fashioned the heavens and the earth.' He made an expansive gesture with his beer bottle and I saw that it was almost empty. He changed tones. 'At least so stand accounts in the oldest creation stories, including the Bible.' He passed me his empty bottle and I immediately replaced it.

'The Bible?' Sean said in surprise.

'Oh, indeed,' and Eppy lifted the replacement in thanks to me before he took a sip. 'The story of the dragon is older even than the Bible. So far as merely human records go, the oldest of all the dragons was named Zu – or Asag, which is obviously the same thing.'

Sean cast a sidelong glance in my direction and arched a brow. 'Obviously . . .'

'Seven thousand years ago,' Eppy continued without noticing, 'the Sumerians related how this already ancient serpent snatched from the great god Enlil the Tablets of the Law. These, of course, regulated the order of the universe. So Enlil sent the sun-god, Ninurta, after him. Or her. It's sometimes hard to tell with Sumerians. Eventually there was, as you would imagine, a terrible fight. But Ninurta finally kills Zu and retrieves the Tablets, thus preventing creation from relapsing into primordial chaos.'

'So right from the beginning, dragons were seen as covetous, thieving, and dangerous,' Sean said glumly.

'For the most part, yes,' Eppy sighed. 'The great enemy from the ancient seas, hostile to both gods and humans.

'One of the oldest of all written accounts, or chiselled actually, since it was carved on clay tablets, is the Babylonian creation epic, the *Enuma elish*. An improvement on the Sumerian version, this old tale contains the saga of Marduk and Tiamat, who surely belonged to the original dysfunctional family.

'The sea-dragons Apsu and his wife Tiamat, also known as Fresh-Water and Salt-Sea, were the parents of the first gods. A couple of generations later, a regrettable but inevitable family misunderstanding leads to a real donnybrook, in which Apsu is slain by one of his great grandsons, the god Enki or Ea. Understandably upset by this, Tiamat rouses her mean and scaly cohorts and resumes Apsu's war against her unruly brood. Marduk, the youngest of the last generation of gods, agrees to fight the old hag, provided that the other gods elect him chief. It wasn't such a bad bargain, given the chances of the lad's surviving.'

'Was Tiamat really a dragon?' I asked.

'In some respects, she is the mother of all dragons,' Eppy grinned. 'The Babylonians originally drew her as a four-leggety beast with the head, shoulders and fore-paws of a lion, a body covered with scales, a pair of feathery wings, hind legs like an eagle's, and a long, forked tongue like a snake's.'

'Sounds like a dragon to me,' I said. 'I'd hate to meet her in a dark cave, somewhere.' I caught Sean's start of alarm.

'Marduk fairly jumps at the chance,' Eppy resumed, oblivious to externals. 'Once holding the reins of power, he assembles a whole godly arsenal. He eventually ensnares his great, great grandam in a magical net. When she opens her maw to devour him, he uses the storm winds to keep her jaws open until he is able to shoot an arrow deep into her vitals. When she is safely dead, the young upstart creates the heavens and the earth out of her remains. He also retrieves the sacred Tablets of Destiny which had been seized by the old lady's chief henchman, grandson, and lover, Kingu.'

13

'That sounds like the other story,' I suggested. 'Who's Kingu?'

'In the ancient drawings, Marduk is always accompanied by a second, smaller dragon running on all fours like a dog. I suspect that's Kingu, the thief. What's important here is the mention, again, of a precious possession that's stolen and retrieved.'

'The . . . hoard?' Sean wondered.

'Exactly,' Eppy beamed. 'The earliest accounts focus on preserving creation against chaos. But gradually the quest for treasure and then the rescue of a princess become more prominent. And don't forget the watery origins. All early dragons are sea-creatures.'

There was no stopping the old *Seannachie Brendan* now.

'Despite twists and turns, the shadow of Tiamat and Marduk falls over almost all subsequent dragons and dragon-killers. A thousand years later, the Hittites of eastern Turkey are telling how the storm-god subdues and kills the mighty dragon Illuyankas with the help of the goddess Inaras and her human lover, Hupasiyas.

'In North Syria, according to the Canaanite *Poem of Baal*, the young god of that name defeats the sea-dragon, Yam-nahar of the Seven Heads. That story in turn influenced important traditions among the Syrians' southern cousins and neighbours – the Assyrians, Medes, Persians, Greeks, and Hebrews, among others.'

'So the old legends all tend to agree,' Sean said. 'More or less.'

'More, more than less,' Eppy nodded. 'Although Egypt's dragon myth differs a bit. It is still concerned with the tension between order and chaos, but not as part of a creation story. Apep or, as he is sometimes known, Apophis, is a huge sea-serpent, the very spirit of darkness and death. He attempts to engulf the sun-god, Atum-Ra, during his voyage across the sky. Apep is attacked and slain by the children of Atum-Ra, the ancient god of Egypt, or, depending on which story you read, by Set alone.

'In whatever case, by the strange logic of the dracomachy, Set not only comes to resemble the enemy he has killed but also takes his place as Ra's nemesis, the evil dragon. Plutarch later tells us that Set is also known as Typhon, who came to figure so prominently in Greek myth.'

'What's a drago – dragomachine?' Sean asked.

'Dracomachy,' I corrected him. 'It's the technical term among dracologists for combat between the god and the dragon. Having one is virtually the law in this business.'

'Aren't there any, er, *peaceful* dragons?' Sean asked.

'Not at this point in the story,' Eppy told him cheerfully.

'Not even in the Bible?'

'I'm coming to that. But first, the Greeks.'

'The Greeks?' Sean looked dazed.

Well, he had asked. I let Eppy go on.

'They not only had a name for it, they gave it to us along with most of the stories we're familiar with. For the Greeks, the primordial serpent was a *drakon*, a word based on the Indo-European root *darc*, meaning "to see clearly." For if anything,

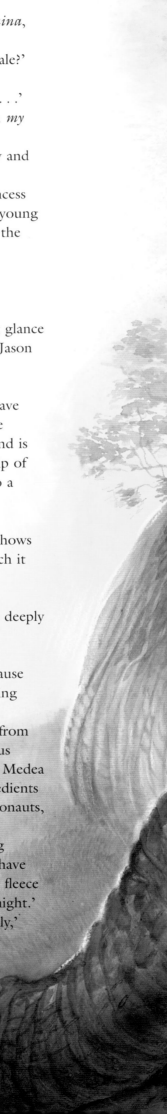

dragons are keen of vision, riveting, and even lethal in their glance. They are also associated with springs. Not surprisingly, the word for spring in many Indo-European and Semitic languages is the same as the word for "eye." There's the water connection, too.

'The Greeks also had a word for a female dragon, *drakaina*, but that didn't come across as well.'

'Perhaps because by then dragons were thought of as male?' I ventured with a sniff at the chauvinism.

'Most of the really famous dragons do seem to be male . . .'

'Which is one reason why the most important dragon in *my* world is female,' I said, unable to resist the comment.

Eppy eyed me sternly at such an interruption to his flow and imperturbably continued.

'. . . Which fits in well with the story of the perilous princess saved from becoming a draconic hors-d'oeuvre by a brave young hero who happens by in the nick of time. At least most of the time.'

'And that's Greek, too?' Sean asked.

'They are somewhat on the romantic side,' Eppy said disparagingly. 'But at first, the princess is not the intended victim, but a very able companion.' Eppy shot me a telling glance of reprimand. 'I think the oldest of these stories is that of Jason and Medea.'

'The Golden Fleece?'

'The very same. As you will remember, Jason and his brave shipmates, the Argonauts, are seeking a fabled treasure, the Golden Fleece, which belongs to King Aeëtes of Colchis and is guarded by a fierce, unsleeping dragon. They enlist the help of Aeëtes' beautiful daughter, the princess Medea, who is also a sorceress.

'Smitten by Jason's good looks and likelihood of career advancement, she makes him promise to marry her if she shows him how to remove the fleece from the sacred oak on which it was hung without becoming a snack for the dragon.'

'Sounds like early hoard material,' Sean suggested.

'Indeed it was. Good watchdogs, dragons. They become deeply attached to whatever they are guarding. Sometimes permanently.'

'I'd heard that dragons are attached to their hoards because the jewels tell them such marvellous tales,' I put in, watching Sean turn a little pale. 'Until the princess appears.'

'Right again. But here the princess is rescuing the hero from the dragon as well as her father, who was a mite treacherous and planned to kill the Argonauts and burn the ship. First, Medea makes a sleeping potion from deadly herbs and other ingredients you're better off not knowing about. Then, one of the Argonauts, Orpheus, lulls the dragon into a gentle slumber with his enchanted lyre. Medea sprinkles the beast with her sleeping potion, but warns Jason not to harm it lest it awaken and have them all for supper. Carefully, the young hero removes the fleece and before the dragon awakens, they all steal off into the night.'

'And into a lot of further trouble, if I remember correctly,' I said.

16

'Stealing from dragons is not without its hazards,' Eppy acknowledged with a quick glance at the curiously intent look on Sean's face. 'But most of the Greeks coped well enough: Apollo battled Delphyne, and then Python, and Zeus himself had to overcome Typhon, the whirlwind. Hercules fought a whole host of them – Archelous, Echidna, Hydra, Ketos, Phorkas, and Skylla, as well as Ladon, who guarded the golden apples of the Hesperides. As he discovered, Greek dragons are notorious shape-shifters, often appearing as human beings – a talent they preserve in many later myths and tales.'

'I'm not too surprised,' Sean said without much enthusiasm. 'How many of them have . . . had . . . hoards?'

'Except for the story of the Golden Fleece, I fear that most of the early ones were after princesses,' Eppy said. 'The most famous of that lot involves the story of Perseus and Andromeda. But in an even earlier story, Hercules rescues Hesione, the daughter of King Laomedon of Troy. And thereby hangs a tale.'

'Why am I not surprised?' I wondered mostly to myself.

'One fine day,' Eppy began, 'the gods Poseidon and Apollo appear to Laomedon and offer, for a price, to provide the city with impregnable walls. Kings being what they are, Laomedon accepts the offer, intending all along to renege on the deal. And when he does, Greek gods being what they are, Apollo sends a plague on the city, and Poseidon calls up a huge sea-monster which begins gobbling up people right and left.

'Worried about losing his own head to the outraged citizens, Laomedon seeks out an oracle. The oracle suggests compensating the offended deities by sacrificing his beautiful young daughter, Hesione, to be eaten by the dragon. Kings being what they are, the poor child is soon chained to a rock to await her doom.

'Luckily for her, Hercules happens to pass by, sizes up the situation, and offers to kill the monster if Laomedon will give him the wonderful horses he had received from Zeus. Herk was a practical lad as well as a wee bit greedy, and already had plenty of lady friends. As usual, Laomedon quickly agrees, and after a vicious battle, Herk kills the dragon and frees poor Hesione.'

'Do they all live happily ever after?'

'The Greeks may have been romantic, but they weren't sentimental,' Eppy said with a glance at Sean. 'True to his nature, Laomedon tries to cheat Herk out of the horses, but succeeds only in bringing down a curse on Troy that leads right up to the Trojan War.'

'Not a very reassuring finale.'

'Those old kings needed periodic reminders about fooling around with divinities and dragons. But they did learn, if somewhat slowly, being what they are. By the time we get to the story of Perseus and Andromeda, the situation is less complicated politically, and people are more interested in romance. So it becomes the model for most subsequent rescue stories, including that of Saint George and *his* dragon.

'The scene shifts to the coast of Philistia, which was later called Palestine. Cassiopeia, the wife of King Cepheus, who seems to have been from Ethiopia, has boasted of her beauty, thereby

insulting the Nereids, who were water-nymphs jealous of their good looks. Nymphs are always beautiful and always jealous. Don't forget that!

'They appeal to Poseidon, who sends a flood and a sea-dragon, Ketos, to ravage the realm. But an oracle announces that if Cepheus gives up his daughter, Andromeda, to be devoured by Ketos, the kingdom would be spared. Kings being what they are, the poor lass is trussed up in a wedding gown and bound to a rock on the beach to await her doom.'

'Sounds familiar,' I said. 'But why the wedding dress?'

'A nice touch, isn't it?' Eppy nodded. 'Old Ketos looks on Andromeda as his bride. Here, the dragon has become the Lord of Death, like Hades. Fortunately, by the same kind of lady-luck that we have seen before, the young hero Perseus passes by, notices the hapless maiden, immediately falls in love, and resolves to save her if she will marry him.'

'Rather better than trading horses,' Sean quipped.

'Everyone thinks it is a good idea,' Eppy continued, unruffled. 'So aided by some handy devices left over from killing Medusa, such as winged sandals for air support, Percy puts paid to Ketos, unfastens the fair Andromeda, gets Cepheus off the hook, and they all live in reasonable contentment. At least for a while.'

'Not happily ever after?' I asked.

'It's not a perfect world.'

'You said there were dragons in the Bible, too?' Sean asked.

'There are plenty of dragons in the Good Book,' Eppy replied. 'Generally, they fare badly. It's pretty likely that Leviathan, who figures in the Book of Job, is the same as Lotan, the Canaanite sea-dragon, who is our old Greek friend Ladon. There are also a number of references in the Book of Psalms and elsewhere to a sea-serpent named Rahab. It seems that when the Almighty divided the waters in the beginning, He also divided what was in them.'

'Divided the dragon, too?'

'Yes, a multi-headed one at that. Generally seven, which makes sense since Yam-nahar and Lotan both had seven heads, too. Do you have the family Bible at hand, my dear?'

From the Canterbury's shelf, I plucked the massive tome and plunked it down in front of the old charmer, almost knocking the pint glasses off the table. Pulling out a pair of half-moon wire spectacles, which he perched on the tip of his nose, Eppy began thumbing through it.

'Ah,' he said only seconds later, 'listen to this: "Thou didst crush the heads of Leviathan, thou didst give him as food for the creatures of the wilderness." That's from the Seventy-fourth Psalm, verse fourteen. It could refer to a whale or crocodile, I suppose, but multiple heads are more consistent with this brand of dragon.'

'What about Rahab?' I asked. I didn't remember that one.

'You'll find her in the fifty-first chapter of Isaiah, among other places: "Was it not Thou that didst cut Rahab in pieces, that didst pierce the dragon?"'

'The Hebrews used other names for the ancient enemy, such as *nachash*, "serpent." It is indeed a nachash, "more subtle than any other wild creature that the Lord God had made" that ambushes the unwary Eve in the Garden. But, as Isaiah makes sure to note, the snake is only a more ancient enemy in disguise: "In that day the Lord with His hard and great and strong sword will punish Leviathan the fleeing nachash, Leviathan the twisting nachash, and he will slay the dragon that is in the sea." '

'Do biblical dragons hoard things?' Sean asked pointedly.

'Well, in a way. They are envious, for sure. In the Greek additions to the Hebrew Bible, Daniel was the hero of the world's first detective story and also a dragon-slayer. In the Story of Bel and the Dragon, Cyrus the Persian, now the King of Babylon, tries to persuade Daniel to worship a big dragon which was the guardian Deity of the city.

' "I worship only the one, true God," Daniel replies. "This monster is only an animal. And if you give me leave to try, I will slay it without using either sword or club."

'The king consents, convinced that Daniel has at last bitten off more than he could chew. It was more likely, in fact, to end up chewing him. But Daniel finds some pitch, fat, and hair, boils them together and makes some German dumplings. He feeds them to the unsuspecting dragon, who eats them and explodes.

' "Now take a look at what you have been worshipping!" Daniel laughs.

'Cyrus is impressed, but the Babylonians think that young Dan has gone too far this time. So they throw him back into the lions' den. There are seven lions in the den, all hungry and used to eating human flesh. But they leave Daniel alone, even when God arranges for the prophet Habakkuk to bring him an order of the world's first fast food. Air-delivered by an angel, you see.' Eppy's eyes twinkled at his wittiness. I sniffed. So Eppy continued, undeterred.

'Seven days later, Cyrus comes around to see what has happened to his young friend. He is, needless to say, impressed when he looks in and finds Daniel fat as a Christmas goose and the lions all lying around with their stomachs rumbling. So he pulls Daniel out, and throws in the men who had planned his demise. As you might have guessed, the lions end up much happier than they do.'

'Not exactly on a par with rescuing maidens,' I said.

'Or, ah, guarding treasure,' Sean amended.

Eppy smiled a crooked little smile. 'Don't be too sure. The use of such imagery to portray the enemies of Israel was passed on to the authors of Christian scripture, and nowhere more vividly than in the Book of Revelation, in which the Hebrew dragon myth, like the Christian Bible and the sinful world itself, come to a grim but not inglorious end.

'In the twelfth chapter, we meet a great red dragon with the requisite seven heads as well as ten horns and seven crowns. The dragon confronts a woman who was about to bear a child; she is clothed with the sun, standing upon the moon, and crowned with twelve stars. His intentions were definitely not benign.

'But, in the guise of an eagle, God rescues both the woman and her child. Then another hero appears in the heavens. The archangel Michael has come to battle the ancient serpent. And by scoring a decisive victory, he becomes fixed in early Christian imagination both as the defender of the Church, symbolized by the faithful but hapless young mother, and also as an implacable enemy of dragons.

'The epic continues in Revelation 12.9, where the great dragon, "that ancient serpent who is called the Devil and Satan, the deceiver of the whole world" is thrown down to the earth, and his angels with him. But even after the dragon is demoted, he continues to pursue the woman who had borne the child.

'True to his draconian nature, he spews a river out of his mouth to sweep the young mother away. This time Michael is unaccountably absent, but the flood is thwarted by God. And like other sea-dragons of the ancient Near East, this one finally receives his just desserts. The Angel of the Pit seizes the ancient serpent and binds him for a thousand years.'

Because I was watching Sean out of the corner of my eye, I saw him start with a keen interest. Eppy went blithely on.

'Ultimately, the poor old devil is thrown into the lake of fire and sulphur with the beast and the false prophet, "where they will be tormented day and night for ever and ever." '

'It's not all that different from the stories of Hercules and Perseus,' I said.

'Ah, but now the dragon is not merely a scourge and threat. He is a manifestation of the very devil himself,' and Eppy raised one finger in emphasis of that point. 'And if these passages seem a bit lacking in Christian compassion, the intense feeling is understandable. After all, in the year AD 70, Jerusalem had been sacked and the Temple destroyed by Titus' legions. For years, they had cut a bloody swath through the Holy Land under the red dragon banner they had adopted from the Parthians and Medes. That emblem was burned indelibly into Christian memory, since the Mother Church and its members perished along with everyone else who did not flee the city.

'But despite Jewish hopes and Christian prophecies, the Red Dragon of Rome was not quite ready to end his violent career in the lake of burning sulphur. A whole tribe of his spawn begin showing up in legends from the Middle East to the Far North.

'Not surprisingly, an entire battery of Christian Saints are soon attacking dragons – Andrew the Apostle and Philip the Deacon, to begin with. In later times, there are also Armand of Maestricht, Bernard of Menton, Cadon of Karnac, Clement of Metz, Donatus, Germanus, Hilarion, Marcel, Naudet of Batz, Pol de Leon, Radegond of Poitiers, Romain of Rouen, Rufinus, Samson of Dol, Saturnin of Bernay, Sylvester (the pope who was a wizard), Theodorus of Heraclea, and of course the more famous dracocides George, Martha, and Margaret.'

'Dracocides?' Sean asked hesitantly.

'The technical term for dragon-slayers,' Eppy explained.

'Dragonsbane being the more modern term,' I inserted.

'But not all saints were hostile,' Eppy continued, looking over his glasses at me in a 'who's-telling-this-anyhow' manner. 'Simon Stylites even cured a dragon.'

'I know someone else, a woman, Jenny Waynest, who did that, too.'

'Wait your turn,' Eppy said. 'A sick dragon had whimpered up to the base of that column, atop which the saint spent most of his adult life for some reason or other. And when he saw that the wretched beast had a splinter in its eye, Simon tenderly removed it.'

I jumped in with my contribution. 'Jenny Waynest cured a dragon from far worse than a mere splinter. Her boyfriend, John Averson, was called upon in his capacity as a dragonsbane to get rid of Black Morkeleb. They have to use poisoned weapons. John is badly wounded also and Jenny realizes that, to save him, she has to find the gnomes' remedies which lie somewhere in the Market Hall beyond the dying dragon.'

The dragon was invisible in the darkness. She heard the soft scrape of his scales and guessed him to be lying across the inner doors of the Market Hall, that led to the Grand Passage and so into the Deep. Then the silver lamps of his eyes opened and seemed to glow softly in the reflected moonlight, and in her mind the singing flowed and intensified its colours into the vortex of a white core. In that core words formed.

Have you come seeking medicines, wizard woman? Or is that weapon you carry simply what you have deluded yourself into thinking sufficient to finish what your poisons do too slowly for your convenience?

The words were almost pictures, music and patterns shaped as much by her own soul as by his. They would hurt, she thought, if allowed to sink too deeply.

'I have come seeking medicines,' she replied, her voice reverberating against the fluted dripstone of the toothed ceiling. 'The power of the Places of Healing was everywhere renowned.'

This I knew. There was a knot of gnomes that held out in the place where they took all the wounded. The door was low, but I could reach through it like a wolf raiding a bury of rabbits. I fed upon them for many days, until they were all gone. They had the wherewithal to make poisons there, too. They had poisoned the carrion, as if they did not think that I could see the death that tainted the meat. This will be the place that you seek.

Because he spoke partially in pictures, she glimpsed also the dark ways into the place, like a half-remembered dream in her mind. Her hope stirred, and she fixed the pictures in her thoughts – tiny fragments, but perhaps enough to serve.

With her wizard's sight she could distinguish him now, stretched before her across the doors in the darkness. He had dislodged the harpoons from his throat and belly, and they lay blackened with his blood in the muck of slime and ash on the floor . . .

I will bargain with you, wizard woman.

She knew, with chill premonition, but no surprise what his bargain would be, and her heart quickened, though whether with dread or some strange hope she did not know. She said, 'No,' but within herself she felt, like a forbidden longing, the unwillingness to let something this beautiful, this powerful, die. He was evil, she told herself, knowing and believing it in her heart. Yet there was something in those silver eyes that drew her, some song of black and latent fire whose music she understood.

The dragon moved his head a little on the powerful curve of his neck. Blood dripped down from the tattered ribbons of his mane.

Do you think that even you, a wizard who sees in the darkness, can search out the ways of the gnomes?

The pictures that filled her mind were of the darkness, of clammy and endless mazes of the world underground. Her heart sank with dread at the awareness of them: those few small images of the way to the Places of Healing, those fragmentary words of Mab's, turned in her hands to the pebbles with which a child thinks it can slaughter lions.

Still she said, 'I have spoken to one of them of these ways.'

And did she tell the truth? The gnomes are not famed for it in matters concerning the heart of the Deep.

Jenny remembered the empty places on Dromar's maps. But she retorted, 'Nor are dragons.'

Beneath the exhaustion and pain, she felt in the dragon's mind amusement at her reply, like a thin spurt of cold water in hot.

What is truth, wizard woman? The truth that dragons see is not pleasant to the human eyes, however uncomfortably comprehensible it may be to their hearts. You know this.

She saw that he had felt her fascination. The silver eyes drew her; his mind touched hers, as a seducer would have touched her hand.

With an effort she tore her eyes from his and turned to leave.

Wizard woman, do you think this man for whom you risk the bones of your body will live longer than I?

She said calmly. 'There is the chance that he will.'

She felt anger in the movement of his head, and the pain that sliced through him with it.

And will you wager on that? Will you wager that, even did the gnomes speak the truth, you will be able to sort your way through their warrens, spiral within spiral, dark within dark, to find what you need in time? Heal me, wizard woman, and I will guide you with my mind and show you the place that you seek.

For a time she only gazed up at that long bulk of shining blackness, the dark mane of bloody ribbons, and the eyes like oiled metal ringing eternal darkness . . . The voice that spoke in her mind was steady, but she could see the weakness dragging at every line of that great body and feel the faint shiver of the last taut strength that fought to continue the bluff against her.

Unwittingly, she said, 'I know nothing of the healing of dragons.'

The silver eyes narrowed, as if she had asked him for something he had not thought to give. For a moment they faced one another, cloaked in the cave's darkness. She was aware of John and of time – distantly, like something urgent in a dream . . .

Then, suddenly, the gleaming body convulsed. She felt, through the silver eyes, the pain like a scream through the steel ropes of his muscles. The wings stretched uncontrollably, the claws extended in a terrible spasm as the poison shifted in his veins. Then the voice in her mind whispered, 'Go'.

At the same moment, memories flooded her thoughts of a place she had never been before. Vague images crowded in her mind of blackness as vast as the night outdoors, columned with a forest of stone trees that whispered back across the echo of every breath, of rock seams a few yards across whose ceilings were lost in distant darkness, and the murmuring of endless water under stone. She felt a vertigo of terror as in a nightmare, but also a queer sense of *déjà vu* as if she had passed that way before.

It came to her that it was Morkeleb, and not she, who had passed that way: the images were the way to the Place of Healing, the very heart of the Deep.[1]

'Did the dragon live?' asked Sean.

I nodded. 'In fact, Morkeleb offers Jenny the chance to *become* a dragon. But that's another story.' I grinned at Eppy for stealing his phrase.

'A most unusual instance,' Eppy blithely remarked. 'Saints, however, were inclined to offer no quarter to dragons.'

'Like St. George?'

'Well, he is the most famous Christian dragon-slayer, but even his reputation . . . er, shall we say, *transcended* the actual facts of the case.'

'A Reluctant Dragon-killer?' I asked demurely.

'Now that *is* a wonderful story.' Eppy beamed. 'Kenneth Grahame's tale, *The Reluctant Dragon*, probably started off the whole revisionist trend to portray both dragons and Holy Knights as bumbling poseurs. Like *The Wind In The Willows*, it is a children's tale, but not a simple one. Here,' he said, pulling out yet another well-used tome, 'see how Grahame reinvents the myth.'

St. George gazed for a while on the fair landscape around them. 'But this would be a beautiful place for a fight,' he began again persuasively. 'These great bare rolling Downs for the arena – and me in my golden armour showing up against your big blue scaly coils! Think what a picture it would make!'

'Now you're trying to get at me through my artistic sensibilities,' said the dragon. 'But it won't work. Not but that it would make a very pretty picture, as you say,' he added, wavering a little.

'We seem to be getting rather nearer to business,' put in the Boy. 'You must see, dragon, that there's got to be a fight of some sort, 'cos you can't want to have to go down that dirty old hole again and stop there till goodness when.'

'It might be arranged,' said St. George thoughtfully. 'I must spear you somewhere, of course, but I'm not bound to hurt you very much. There's such a lot of you that there must be a few spare places somewhere. Here, for instance, just behind your foreleg. It couldn't hurt you much, just here!'

'Now you're tickling, George,' said the dragon coyly. 'No, that place won't do at all. Even if it didn't hurt – and I'm sure it would, awfully – it would make me laugh, and that would spoil everything.'

'Let's try somewhere else, then,' said St. George patiently. 'Under your neck, for instance – all these folds of thick skin – if I speared you here you'd never even know I'd done it!'

'Yes, but are you sure you can hit off the right place?' asked the dragon anxiously.

'Of course I am,' said St. George, with confidence. 'You leave that to me!'

'It's just because I've got to leave it to you that I'm asking,' replied the dragon rather testily. 'No doubt you would deeply regret any error you might make in the hurry of the moment; but you wouldn't regret it half as much as I should! However, I suppose we've got to trust somebody, as we go through life, and your plan seems, on the whole, as good a one as any.'

'Look here, dragon,' interrupted the Boy, a little jealous on behalf of his friend, who seemed to be getting all the worst of the bargain: 'I don't quite see where you come in! There's to be a fight, apparently, and you're to be licked; and what I want to know is, what are you going to get out of it?'

'St. George,' said the dragon, 'just tell him, please – what will happen after I'm vanquished in the deadly combat?'

'Well, according to the rules, I suppose I shall lead you in triumph down to the market-place or whatever answers to it,' said St. George.

'Precisely,' said the dragon. 'And then . . .?'

'And then there'll be shoutings and speeches and things,' continued St. George. 'And I shall explain that you're converted, and see the error of your ways, and so on.'

'Quite so,' said the dragon. 'And then . . .?'

'Oh, and then' – said St. George, 'why, and then there will be the usual banquet, I suppose.'

'Exactly,' said the dragon; 'and that's where I come in. Look here,' he continued, addressing the Boy, 'I'm bored to death up here, and no one really appreciates me. I'm going into Society, I am, through the kindly aid of our friend here, who's taking such a lot of trouble on my account; and you'll find I've got all the qualities to endear me to people who entertain! So now that's all settled, and if you don't mind – I'm an old-fashioned fellow – don't want to turn you out, but . . .'

'Remember, you'll have to do your proper share of the fighting, dragon!' said St. George, as he took the hint and rose to go; 'I mean ramping, and breathing fire, and so on!'

'I can ramp all right,' replied the dragon confidently; 'as to breathing fire, it's surprising how easily one gets out of practice; but I'll do the best I can. Good night!'

They had descended the hill and were almost back in the village again, when St. George stopped short. 'Knew I had forgotten something,' he said. 'There ought to be a Princess. Terror-stricken and chained to a rock, and all that sort of thing. Boy, can't you arrange a Princess?'

The Boy was in the middle of a tremendous yawn. 'I'm tired to death,' he wailed, 'and I can't arrange a Princess, or anything more, at this time of night. And my mother's sitting up, and do stop asking me to arrange more things till tomorrow.'

'So the whole thing was a fraud?'

'Well, not exactly a fraud.' Eppy had a mischievous twinkle in his eye. 'Perhaps it would be better to describe it as an act of mutual tolerance and forebearance. Here is how the battle turned out.'

St. George now shortened his spear, bringing the butt well up under his arm; and, instead of galloping as before, trotted smartly towards the dragon, who crouched at his approach, flicking his tail till it cracked in the air like a great cart-whip. The Saint wheeled as he neared his opponent and circled warily round him, keeping his eye on the spare place; while the dragon, adopting similar tactics, paced with caution round the same circle, occasionally feinting with his head. So the two sparred for an opening, while the spectators maintained a breathless silence.

Though the round lasted for some minutes, the end was so swift that all the Boy saw was a lightning movement of the Saint's arm, and then a whirl and confusion of spines, claws, tail, and flying bits of turf. The dust cleared away, the spectators whooped and ran in cheering, and the Boy made out that the dragon was down, pinned to the earth by the spear, while St. George had dismounted, and stood astride of him.

It all seemed so genuine that the Boy ran in breathlessly, hoping the dear old dragon wasn't really hurt. As he approached, the dragon lifted one large eyelid, winked solemnly, and collapsed again. He was held fast to earth by the neck, but the Saint had hit him in the spare place agreed upon, and it didn't even seem to tickle.

'Bain't you goin' to cut 'is 'ed orf, mister?' asked one of the applauding crowd. He had backed the dragon, and naturally felt a trifle sore.

'Well, not today, I think,' replied St. George pleasantly. 'You see, that can be done at any time. There's no hurry at all. I think we'll all go down to the village first, and have some refreshment, and then I'll give him a good talking-to, and you'll find he'll be a very different dragon!'

At that magic word refreshment the whole crowd formed up in procession and silently awaited the signal to start.[2]

'You see, Grahame's revision of the old tale still assumes that there was an encounter. In all probability, the only dragon St. George ever heard about was in the story of Perseus and Andromeda. The real George seems to have been from Cappadocia, up in modern Turkey. And he may well have become a soldier in the army of Diocletian, as one legend has it, who was martyred at Lydda in Palestine around the year AD 303

'Like most martyrs, George soon acquired a circle of enthusiastic admirers. By the sixth century, a fictional account of his relatively brief life and heroic death had been translated into six languages. By the eighth century, his fame had even reached England. His name appears in the Irish *Martyrology of Oengus* about the same time. By then, popular tradition had firmly linked George with Perseus, who had killed *his* dragon near Lydda at Joppa, where George's tomb was supposedly discovered during the First Crusade. It was the right neighbourhood, after all, and Perseus admittedly added a certain panache that George lacked.'

'But isn't that . . . cheating?' I demanded for I hadn't heard *that* about dear ol' St. George.

'Not at all. Happens all the time. In the ancient Christian *Acta*

Philippi, St. Philip gets to fight the dragon, Echidna, in place of Apollo. It goes with being a local hero.

'In any case, George's great popularity with the first Crusaders undoubtedly accelerated his amalgamation with Perseus. Eventually, his fame (and the dragon's, too) outstripped not only that of Perseus, but also of other Christian Saints and even the Archangel Michael. In England alone, more than 160 ancient churches were dedicated to St. George.

'The oldest version of the story known to me is from Yemen, and it also comes closest to the legend of Perseus and Andromeda. The Arab Christians there tell how there was once a great city which depended totally for water on a spring outside its walls. But a fierce dragon, undoubtedly possessed by Satan, occupied the oasis and refused to allow anyone to draw water unless a youth or maiden was given to him to devour. The distraught citizens tried to kill the awful beast several times, but its breath was so noxious that anyone who approached was quickly overcome and died.

'One by one, the flower of the city disappeared into the dragon's mouth. Finally, only the king's daughter herself was

left. Crazed by thirst, the people pressured the king into sacrificing his only child.'

'Let me guess,' I said. 'She has to put on a wedding dress.'

'Indeed,' Eppy nodded somberly. 'But just as she was about to be gobbled up, a handsome young soldier rode by on a fine white horse. His name was Mar Jirys – which, of course, means St. George. Spurring his charger toward the vile serpent, he thrust his lance into its heart and killed it. Overjoyed, the king gave Mar Jirys his daughter's hand in marriage as well as half his kingdom.'

'It does sound a bit familiar,' I said.

'Later versions are more elaborate, of course. In the Middle Ages, Jacob of Voragine's highly successful and romantic book of saintly exploits, *The Golden Legend*, sets the scene in Libya, although I think Jake may have just misspelled Lydda. The dragon now lives in a cave and simply demands daily rations of sheep from the terrified townspeople. And when supplies run low, young virgins. The lot falls on the king's daughter, Sabra, who is dressed in a bridal gown and exposed near the cave.'

'There seems to be a pattern there, all right,' I said.

'A clue, actually. It's all about Love and Death. The oldest quarrel in the world. Luckily for Sabra, George happens by

looking for good deeds to do, and, smitten by the girl's plight, not to mention her beauty, skewers the dragon outright, or, in other versions of the story, wounds it severely enough for it to be led into town. There, George reassures the grateful populace that they had been delivered by the grace of God and chops off the dragon's head to prove it. As a reward, he is permitted to baptize fifteen thousand people, including the king and Sabra.

'Unlike Perseus and Mar Jirys, however, George does not get to marry Sabra. As in an old cowboy movie, he rides off into the sunset towards Palestine, where after many adventures he is duly martyred at Joppa under the governor Dacian.'

'What happened to Sabra?'

'Jacob doesn't say.'

'I liked the story of Mar Jirys better. But why didn't the dragon breathe fire?' Sean asked.

'That comes later. Earlier dragons mainly had very severe halitosis,' Eppy said.

'You mean they had to *learn* to breathe fire?' I asked. 'Mine are *born* knowing *that*!'

'They are?' Sean looked at me with some surprise. 'I was told you were an expert on dragons. I didn't know you had your own.'

'Oh, definitely. The Pernese dragon. Unique. They eat a phosphine-bearing rock, and digest it in a second stomach . . .' I stifled a grin as Sean's eyes bugged out.

On the rim of Benden Weyr, the dragons had assembled, ready to fight their ancient enemy, Thread, and roared the challenge. Mnementh, the great bronze, raised his head, echoing back the brass thunder of the war cry. He turned his head to F'lar, even as hundreds of other beasts turned their heads to their riders. Hundreds of great jaws masticated the stone, then swallowed it, their digestive acids transforming dry stone into flame-producing gases, igniting on contact with oxygen.

Well, he'd said he was a farmer and cows have two stomachs. 'And when the meal makes them belch, the phosphine gas ignites when it hits oxygen.'

'Yes, I suppose it would at that,' Sean said, blinking in surprise at such a logical and chemical explanation.

'Robert Heinlein used methane for his dragons,' I went on.

'Chickens produce methane.'

'Dragons are *not* chickens,' I said. 'Although,' and I reached to my so-conveniently placed shelf of dragon books, 'the *best* source of draconic fire is in Terry Pratchett's Ankh-Morpork.' I had the page marked there, too. 'The most ingenous of fire-breathers is the swamp-dragon, Errol Goodboy, Bindle Featherstone of Quirm.'

'Who?' Sean was clearly confused so I repeated the full pedigree again before I read out the passage.

No wonder swamp-dragons were always ill. They relied on permanent stomach trouble for supplies of fuel. Most of their brain power was taken up with controlling the complexities of their digestion which could distill flame-producing fuels from the most unlikely ingredients. They could even rearrange their internal plumbing overnight to deal with difficult processes. They lived on a chemical knife-edge the whole time. One misplaced hiccup and they were geography.

I flipped to the next page, holding up my free hand to deter Eppy from interrupting.

Our hero Errol Goodboy sat . . . swaying and moaning softly. White smoke rolled slowly from his ears and drifted toward the floor. From somewhere inside his swollen stomach came complex explosive hydraulic noises, as though desperate teams of gnomes were trying to drive a culvert through a cliff in a thunderstorm.

'Bear with me . . . because Errol Goodboy has the most marvelous fight with a *draconis nobilis*, that someone in Ankh-Morpork aroused and now it's hoping to get the world back.' I found the pages easily.

The dragon kennels exploded. The windows blew out. The door left the wall ahead of a great billow of black smoke and sailed into the air, tumbling slowly, to plough into the rhododendrons.

Something very energetic and hot was happening in the building . . . Swamp-dragons shot determinedly out of the wreckage like champagne corks, wings whirring frantically.

Still the smoke unrolled. But there was something in there, some point of fierce white light that was gently rising.

It disappeared from view as it passed a stricken window and then, with a piece of roof tile still spinning on top of his head, Errol climbed above his own smoke and ascended into the skies of Ankh-Morpork.

They can rearrange their own plumbing, Vimes told himself bemusedly. To suit circumstances. He's made it work in reverse . . . No wonder the little bugger has got such stubby wings. His body must have known he wasn't going to need them, except to steer.

Good grief. I'm watching the first ever dragon to flame *backwards*.

He risked a glance immediately above him. The great dragon was frozen, its enormous bloodshot eyes concentrating on the tiny creature.

With a challenging roar of flame and a pummelling of air the King of Ankh-Morpork rose, all thought of mere humans forgotten . . .

'How do they fight?' (Vimes) asked Lady Ramkin.

'I – that is, well, they just flap at each other and blow flame,' she said. 'Swamp-dragons, that is. I mean, who's ever seen a noble dragon fight?' . . . Flames roared into the space where Errol had been, but he wasn't there. The king tried to spin in mid-air. The little dragon circled in an easy series of smoke rings, weaving a cat's cradle in the sky with the huge adversary gyrating helplessly in the middle. More flames, hotter and longer, stabbed at him and missed.

'What do you mean, it's not going to work?' said Vimes. 'Look at (Errol) go! It hasn't hit him yet!'

'Yes, but his flame has touched it several times. It doesn't seem to have any effect. It's not hot enough, I think. Oh, he's dodging well. But he's got to be lucky every time. *It* has only got to be lucky once.'

'You mean,' said Vimes, 'all this is just – just show? He's just doing it to *impress*?'

'S'not his fault,' said Colon, materializing behind them. 'It's like dogs init? Doesn't really dawn on the poor little bugger that he's up against a big one. He's just ready for a scrap.'

Both dragons appeared to realize that this fight was the well-known Klatchian stand-off. With another smoke ring and a billow of white flames they parted and retreated a few hundred yards.

The king hovered, flapping its wings quickly. Height. That was the thing. When dragon fought dragon, height was always the thing.

Errol balanced on his flame. He seemed to be thinking.

Then he nonchalantly kicked his back legs out, as though hovering on your own stomach gases was something dragons had mastered over millions of years, somersaulted, and fled. For a moment he was visible as a silver streak, and then he was out over the city walls and gone.

 . . . Overhead the great dragon strutted through the air and flamed a nearby tower. It had won.

'I've never seen that before,' said Lady Ramkin. 'Dragons normally fight to the death.'

'At last they've bred one who's sensible,' said Vimes morosely. 'Let's be honest: the chances of a dragon the size of Errol beating something that big are a million-to-one.'

There was one of those silences you get after one clear bright note has been struck and the world pauses . . .

Nobby nudged (Vimes) in the ribs and pointed across the plain.

There *was* a column of black smoke out there. Vimes squinted. Running ahead of the smoke, speeding over the cabbage fields and closing fast, was a silvery bullet.

The great dragon had seen it too. It flamed defiance and climbed for extra height, mashing the air with its enormous wings.

Now Errol's flame was visible, so hot as to be almost blue. The landscape rolled away underneath him at an impossible speed, and he was accelerating.

Ahead of him the king extended its claws. It was almost grinning.

Errol's going to hit it, Vimes thought. Gods help us all, it'll be a fireball.

Something odd was happening in the fields. A little way behind Errol, the ground appeared to be ploughing itself up, throwing cabbage stalks into the air. A hedgerow erupted in a shower of sawdust.

Errol passed silently over the city walls, nose up, wings folded down to tiny flaps, his body honed to a mere cone with a flame at one end. His opponent blew out a tongue of fire: Vimes watched Errol, with a barely noticeable flip of a wing stub, roll easily out of its path. And then he was gone, speeding out toward the sea in the same eerie silence.

'He miss . . .' Nobby began.

The air ruptured. An endless thunderclap of noise dragged across the city, smashing tiles, toppling chimneys. In mid-air, the king was picked up, flattened out and spun like a top in the sonic wash. Vimes, his hands over his own ears, saw the creature flame desperately as it turned and became the centre of a spiral of crazy fire.

Magic crackled along its wings. It screamed like a distressed foghorn. Then, shaking its head dazedly, it began to glide in a wide circle.

Vimes groaned. It had survived something that tore masonry apart. What did you have to *do* to beat it? You can't fight it, he thought. You can't burn it, you can't smash it. There's nothing you can do.

The dragon landed. It wasn't a perfect landing. A perfect landing wouldn't have demolished a row of cottages. It was slow, and it seemed to go on for a long time and rip up a considerable stretch of city.

Wings flapping aimlessly, neck waving and spraying random flame, it ploughed through a debris of beams and thatch. Several fires started up along the trail of destruction.

Finally it came to rest at the end of the furrow, almost invisible under a heap of former architecture . . .

More rubble moved as the dragon strained to get up. There was a thump as a heavy beam was shouldered aside. The crowd began to run for it.

It was at this point that Errol came back over the rooftops in a series of minor explosions, leaving a trail of smoke rings. Dipping low, he buzzed the crowd and sent the front rank stumbling backwards.

He was also wailing like a foghorn.

Vimes grabbed Carrot and stumbled down the heap as the king started to scrabble desperately to get free.

'He's come back for the kill,' he shouted. 'It probably took him all this time just to slow down.'[3]

'One doesn't need to be massive to do the job,' Eppy said tolerantly. 'I was talking about the ancient ones from which all modern variations stem. Including yours.'

'Point taken,' I said graciously.

'Thank you,' and then Eppy turned deferentially to Sean, ignoring me. 'I'll explain what *I* mean later.'

'And what about hoards?' Sean asked, back to that subject again. I was beginning to wonder just what sort of a hoard he had that had prompted all this.

'For people living in the desert, water is very precious,' Eppy went on, ignoring that direct query, too. 'And, as you recall . . .'

'Dragons are associated with water,' Sean, good student and listener that he was, said. 'I remember.'

'Springs, lakes, rivers, wells, and fountains. But the maiden is also important. I should add that in those medieval Christian stories, it wasn't only the knight in shining armour who overcame the dragon. Sometimes the young woman herself did.'

'Now that *is* interesting!' I couldn't repress myself. 'Does she save the knight?'

29

'Not at this stage of draconic development. The two most famous lady dragon-fighters, St. Margaret and St. Martha, stand pretty much on their own.

'Just who St. Martha was remains open to question. But she is fondly remembered for halting the depredations of a particularly nasty dragon who ravaged the countryside in early Christian Gaul. He is usually called *la Tarasque*. His downfall is accomplished when Martha applies a healthy dash of holy water to his hide. Soundly upbraided by the Saint, the savage reptile even repents of his misdeeds.'

'Could the story be a hint that some aspects of pagan belief were seen as compatible with the gospel?'

'Possibly. But unfortunately for early ecumenism, another version of the legend relates that the grateful townsfolk quickly put the poor Tarasque to death. In any case, as a ceremonial prop, the old serpent remained an essential part of Tarascon festivals until fairly recent times.'

'I know an even better one,' I said firmly, since I could now put Eppy in his place for serving up so many maidens to dragons. I eyed him sternly to give way to me for a bit. I reached for the appropriate book and, from much use, it fell open to the right page. 'My good friend Aerin,' I said.

The petition reported a dragon, destroying crops and killing chickens. It had also badly burned a child who had accidentally discovered its lair, although the child had been rescued in time to save its life. Arlbeth sighed and rubbed his face with his hand. 'Very well. We will send someone to deal with it.'

The man bowed and left.

'There will be more of them now, with the trouble at the Border,' said Tor. 'That sort of vermin seems to breed faster when the North wind blows.'

'I fear you are right,' Arlbeth replied. 'and we can ill spare anyone just now.'

'I'll go,' said Tor.

'Up to the present century, there were also a number of English snap-dragons, as they were called. Several are now in museums. People dressed up in dragon suits that sometimes had all sorts of wonderful mechanical contrivances on board that enabled them to flap their wings, puff smoke, and roar. But like the dragons in Chinese New Year parades, they didn't eat anyone. Not really.

'St. Margaret, on the other hand, was allowed to be devoured by a dragon as a quaint form of martyrdom. As the story goes, however, her innocence equips her to survive and she emerges whole and entire from the dragon's cleft body in a miraculous rebirth reminiscent of Jonah's escape from the whale. But, in this instance, the dragon doesn't survive the ordeal.

'Margaret wasn't the first to survive being gobbled down whole, of course.' Eppy was enjoying this part too much, I thought. 'Hercules and other heroes, who were anything but innocent young maidens, managed to hack their way out of dragons' bellies after being eaten alive. But so far as I know, Margaret is the only heroine to do so, especially bare-handed.'

'A formidable young lady,' Sean commented. 'Rather a far cry from the helpless princess on the beach.'

'Don't be a fool,' snapped the king, and then immediately said, 'I'm sorry. I can spare you least of all – as you know. Dragons don't kill people very often any more, but dragonslayers rarely come back without a few uncomfortable burns.'

'Someday,' said Tor with a wry smile, 'when we have nothing better to do, we must think up a more efficient way to cope with dragons. It's hard to take them seriously – but they are a serious nuisance.'

Aerin sat very still.

'Yes.' Arlbeth frowned into his malak. 'I'll ask tomorrow for half a dozen volunteers to go take care of this. And pray it's an old slow one.'

Aerin also prayed it was an old slow one as she slipped off. She had only a day's grace, so she needed to leave at once; fortunately she had visited the village in question once on a state journey with her father, so she knew more or less how to get there. It was only a few hours' ride.

Her hands shook as she saddled Talat and tied the bundles of dragon-proof suit, kenet, sword and a spear – which she wasn't at all sure she could use, since, barring a few lessons from Tor when she was eight or nine years old, she was entirely self-taught – to the saddle. Then she had to negotiate her way past the stable, the castle, and down the king's way out of the city, without anyone trying to stop her; and the sword and spear, in spite of the long cloak she had casually laid over them, were a bit difficult to disguise.

Her luck – or something – was good. She was worrying so anxiously about what she would say if stopped that she gave herself a headache; but as she rode, everyone seemed to be looking not quite in her direction – almost as if they couldn't quite *see* her, she thought. It made her feel a little creepy. But she got out of the City unchallenged.

The eerie feeling, and the headache, lifted at once when she and Talat set off through the forest below the City. The sun was shining, and the birds seemed to be singing just for her. Talat lifted into a canter, and she let him run for a while, the wind slipping through her hair, the shank of the spear tapping discreetly at her leg, reminding her that she was on her way to accomplish something useful.

She stopped at a little distance from the dragon-infested village to put on her suit – which was no longer quite so greasy; it had reached its

She was wondering how she could tell them delicately that she didn't want them hanging around to watch, since she wasn't at all sure how graceful (or effective) her first encounter with a real dragon was likely to be. But the villagers who accompanied her to show her the way had no intention of getting anywhere near the scene of the battle; a cornered dragon was not going to care what non-combatant bystanders it happened to catch with an ill-aimed lash of fire. They pointed the way, and then returned to their village to wait on events.

Aerin hung her sword round her waist, settled the spear into the crook of her arm. Talat walked with his ears sharply forward, and when he

saturation point, perhaps, and then adapted, as well-oiled boots adapt to the feet that wear them. Her suit still quenched torches, but it had grown as soft and supple as cloth, and almost as easy to wear. She rubbed ointment on her face and her horse, and pulled on her long gloves. Shining rather brightly in the sunlight then and reeking of pungent herbs, Aerin rode into the village.

Talat was unmistakably a war-horse, even to anyone who had never seen one before, and her red hair immediately identified her as the first sol. A little boy stood up from his doorstep and shouted: 'they're here for the dragon!' And then there were a dozen, two dozen folk in the street, looking at her, and then looking in puzzlement for the five or six others that should have been riding with her.

'I am alone,' said Aerin; she would have liked to explain, not that she was here without her father's knowledge but that she was alone because she was dragon-proof (she hoped) and didn't need any help. But her courage rather failed her, and she didn't. In fact what the villagers saw as royal pride worked very well, and they fell over themselves to stop appearing to believe that a first sol (even a half-foreign one) couldn't handle a dragon by herself (and if her mother really was a witch, maybe there was some good in her being half a foreigner after all) and several spoke at once, offering to show the way to where the dragon made its lair, a lot of them careful not to look again down the road behind her.

snorted she smelled it too: fire and something else. It was a new smell, and it was the smell of a creature that did not care if the meat it ate was fresh or not, and was not tidy with the bones afterward. It was the smell of dragon.

Talat, after his warning snort, paced onward carefully. They came soon to a little clearing with a hummock of rock at its edge. The hummock had a hole in it, the upper edge of which was rimmed with greasy smoke. The litter of past dragon meals was scattered across the once green meadow, and it occurred to Aerin that the footing would be worse for a horse's hard hoofs than a dragon's sinewy claws.

Talat halted, and they stood, Aerin gazing into the black hole in the hill. A minute or two went by and she wondered, suddenly, how one got the dragon to pay attention to one in the first place. Did she have to wake it up? Yell? Throw water into the cave at it?

Just as her spearpoint sagged with doubt, the dragon hurtled out of its den and straight at them: and it opened its mouth and blasted them with its fire – except that Talat had never doubted, and was ready to step nimbly out of its way as Aerin scrabbled with her spear and grabbed at Talat's mane to keep from falling off onto the dragon's back. It spun round – it was about the height of Talat's knees, big for a dragon and dreadfully quick on its yellow-clawed feet – and sprayed fire at them again. This time, although Talat got them out of the worst of it, it licked over her arm. She

saw the fire wash over the spear handle and glance off her elbow, but she did not feel it and the knowledge that her ointment did accomplish what it was meant to do gave her strength and cleared her mind. She steadied the spear-butt and nudged Talat with one ankle; as he side-stepped and as the dragon whirled round at them again, she threw her spear.

It wouldn't have been a very good cast for a member of the thotor, or for a seasoned dragon-hunter, but it served her purpose. It stuck in the dragon's neck, in the soft place between neck and shoulder where the scales are thin, and it slowed the dragon down. It twitched and lashed its tail and roared at her, but she knew she hadn't given it a mortal wound: if she let it skulk off to its lair, it would eventually heal and re-emerge, nastier than ever.

It bent itself around the wounded shoulder and tried to grip the spear in its teeth, which were long and thin and sharp and not well suited for catching hold of anything so smooth and hard and narrow as a spearshaft. Aerin dismounted and pulled out her sword, and approached it warily. It ignored her, or appeared to, till she was quite close; and then it snapped its long narrow head around at her again and spat fire.

It caught her squarely; and dragonfire had none of the friendliness of a woodfire burning by the side of the river. The dragonfire pulled at her, seeking her life; it clawed at her pale shining skin, and at the supple leather she wore, and while the heat of it did not distress her, the heat of its malice did, and as the fire passed over and disappeared she stood still in shock, and stared straight ahead of her and did not move.

The dragon knew it had killed her. It was an old dragon, and had killed one or two human beings, and knew that it had caught this one well and thoroughly. It had been a bit puzzled that she did not scream when it burned her arm, and that she did not scream now and fall down writhing on the earth; but this did not matter. She would not trouble it further, and it could attend to its sore shoulder.

Aerin took half a dozen stiff steps forward, grasped the end of the spear and forced the dragon to the ground, swung her sword up and down, and cut off the dragon's head.

Then there was an angry scream from Talat, and she whirled, the heat of the dead dragon's freshly spilled blood rising as steam and clouding her vision, but she saw dragonfire and she saw Talat rear and strike with his forefeet.

She ran toward them and thought, Gods, help me, it had a mate; I forgot, often there are two of them, and she chopped at the second dragon's tail, and missed. It swung around, breathing fire, and she felt the heat of it across her throat, and then Talat struck at it again. It lashed her with its tail when it whirled to face the horse again, and Aerin tripped and fell, and the dragon was on top of her at once, the claws scrabbling at her leather tunic and the long teeth fumbling for her throat. The smoke from its nostrils hurt her eyes. She yelled, frantically, and squirmed under the dragon's weight; and she heard something tear, and she knew if she was caught in dragonfire again she would be burned.

Then Talat thumped into the dragon's side with both hind feet, and the force of the blow lifted them both – for the dragon's claws were tangled in leather laces – and dropped them heavily. The dragon coughed, but there was no fire, and Aerin had fallen half on top of the thing. It raked her with its spiked tail, and something else tore, and its teeth snapped together inches from her face. Her sword was too long: she could not get it close enough for stabbing, and her shoulder was tiring. She dropped the sword and struggled to reach her right boot-top, where she had a short dagger, but the dragon rolled, and she could not reach it.

Then Talat was there again, and he bit the dragon above its small red eye, where the ear hole was; and the dragon twisted its neck to spout fire

at him, but it was still dazed by its fall and only a little fire came out of its mouth. Talat plunged his own face into the trickle of smoke and seized the dragon by the nostrils and dragged its head back; and still farther back. Its forefeet and breast came clear of the ground, and as the dragon thrashed, Aerin's leg came free, and she pulled the dagger from her boot and thrust it into the dragon's scaleless breast. The dragon shrieked, the noise muffled by Talat's grip on its nose, and Aerin stumbled away to pick up her sword.

Talat swung the dying dragon back and forth, and slashed at its body with one forefoot, and the muscles of his heavy stallion's neck ran with sweat and smudges of ash. Aerin lifted the sword and sliced the dragon's belly open, and it convulsed once, shuddered, and died. Talat dropped the body and stood with his head down, shivering, and Aerin realized what she had done, and how little she had known about what it would involve, and how near she had come to failure; and her stomach rebelled, and she lost what remained of her breakfast over the smoking mutilated corpse of the second dragon.

She walked a few steps away till she came to a tree, and with her hands on its bole she felt her way to the ground, and sat with her knees drawn up and her head between them for a few minutes. Her head began to clear, and her breathing slowed, and as she looked up and blinked vaguely at the leaves overhead, she heard Talat's hoofbeats behind her. She put out a hand, and he put his bloody nose into it, and so they remained for several heartbeats more, and then Aerin sighed and stood up. 'Even dragons need water. Let's look for a stream.'[4]

'She was, of course, perfectly correct in remarking that dragons need water,' Eppy said, rocking forward now to take up the narration, almost as if I hadn't had my say. 'However, despite the valor and cleverness of the women, it appears that most successful dragon-slayers were men. Not every medieval hero is an avatar of St. George, of course. But some clearly are, including Tristran, Lancelot, Gawain, and Ruggiero, who saves Angelica in Ariosto's *Orlando Furioso*. Other heroes include the Danish prince Ragnar Shaggy-Legs, who fought the dragons of Herodd; the Byzantine Digenes Akrites; Deodatus de Gozona, who fought the Dragon of Rhodes; Spenser's Red Cross Knight; the Romanian knight Stan Bolovan; as well as Childe Wynd and Childe Lambton in England.

'There were plenty of dragon-slayers elsewhere who also benefited from George's example.'

'Did you know that dragon-slayers were referred to as "Georges" by dragons?' I asked in my brightest rhetorical manner. Eppy glared at me.

'All right, who?' He took the bait.

'I've got the book right here,' I said and took it down, clearing my throat to read.

'Blast it, Gorbash!' roared the voice he [Jim] had been trying to ignore. 'Wake up! Come on, boy, we've got to get down to the main cave. They've just captured one.'

'One . . .?' Jim stammered. 'One what?'

An enormous head with crocodile-sized jaws equipped with larger-than-crocodile-sized fangs thrust itself between Jim's eyes and the ceiling.

'I'm awake. I – ' What he was seeing suddenly registered on Jim's stunned mind and he burst out involuntarily, 'A dragon!'

'And just what would you expect your maternal grand-uncle to be, a sea lizard? Or are you having nightmares again? Wake up. It's Smrgol talking to you, boy. Smrgol. Come on, shake a wing and get flapping. They'll be expecting us in the main cave. Isn't every day we capture a George. Come on, now.'

The fanged mouth whirled away. Blinking, Jim dropped his eyes from the vanishing apparition and caught sight of a huge tail, an armoured tail with a row of sharp, bony plates running along its upper surface. It swelled larger as it approached him . . .

It was his tail.

He held up his arms in front of them. They were enormous. Also, they were thickly scaled with bony plates like those on his tail but much smaller – and his claws needed manicuring. Squinting at the claws, Jim became aware of a long muzzle stretching down and out from where his formerly 'invisible' nose had been. He licked dry lips and a long, red, forked tongue darted out briefly in the smoky air.

'*Gorbash!*' thundered the voice once more; and Jim looked to see the other dragon face glaring at him from a stone doorway. It was in fact, he saw, the entrance to the cave he was in. 'I'm on my way. Catch up or not – it's up to you.'

The other disappeared and Jim shook his head, bewildered. What was going on here? According to Grottwold, no one else was supposed to be able to see him, let alone . . .

Dragons?

Dragons who talked . . .?

To say nothing of his being – he, Jim Eckhert – himself a dragon . . .

That was the absolutely ridiculous part. He, a dragon? How could he be a dragon? Why would he be a dragon, even if there *were* such things as dragons? The whole thing must be some sort of hallucination.

Of course! He remembered, now. Grottwold had mentioned that what he would seem to be experiencing would be entirely subjective. What he was apparently seeing and hearing must be nothing more than a sort of nightmare, overlying whatever real place and people he had reached. A dream. He pinched himself.

And jumped.

He had forgotten about noticing his 'fingers' had claws on them. Large claws, and very sharp ones. If what he was experiencing was a dream, the elements of that dream were damned real.[5]

'Such an experience would have been seriously disorienting,' Eppy said, surprised at having enjoyed the excerpt.

'There's a tad more. Bear with me,' I said, as I caught Eppy before he could launch himself again. 'Jim Eckert gets quite accustomed to his draconic shape and, in the course of the story, takes part against the enemy, Sir Hugh, who's not only attacking dragons but has abducted Jim's girlfriend.'

The dragon-fury was now completely in possession of Jim. He leaped from the wall at this new body of the enemy. None of them had been looking up and he cannoned into them without warning. Suddenly he was in the midst of battle, hissing, roaring, fighting with teeth, claws and wings all at once, balanced on his hind legs like some gigantic bird of prey.

They melted about him. It was like battling straw men armed with candy-cane weapons. The pikes broke at his touch: he flung men who carried them about like dolls. A savage feeling of power flamed up in him. Out of the corner of one eye he saw Aragh again surrounded by a fresh group of Sir Hugh's retainers and thought of going to the wolf's aid as soon as he had

finished matters where he was. What was it Aragh had said about seeing that Gorbash got back safely? But Jim needed nobody's help. Who could stand against a dragon? No one. He was invincible, and when this was over he would remind them all of that – wolf, outlaws, knight . . . Then, abruptly the men at arms who had been attacking him began to shout and yell triumphantly.

'Gorbash!' howled Aragh. '*Gorbash!*'

Jim looked, between the pikeheads that came flashing at him suddenly with renewed vigour. The main doors of the hall were opening; and slowly, as he watched, a ponderous figure all in mirror-bright armour, already mounted with a long lance in one gauntleted hand, rode out through the opening.

The armoured figure did not appear to be in a hurry. It rode out into the centre of the courtyard, turned its head in the direction of the wolf, looked toward Jim, then put its horse into a leisurely trot and rode – not at either one, but out of the castle gate.

'Too late,' Jim thundered, joyously. 'I spoke for him first.'

He took to his wings, lifting up and over the wall. Outside the armoured figure on the horse was already three-quarters of the way to the forest edge.

'Surrender, Sir Hugh!' shouted Jim at full volume. 'I'll get you anyway.'

He had expected the escaping knight, particularly after showing he was the kind to leave his men to die while he saved himself, to do nothing but put his heavy roan into a panic-stricken gallop at the sound of a dragon-voice and the sight of dragon-wings swooping after him. To Jim's surprise, however, Sir Hugh pulled his steed to a stop, turned and lowered his lance to attack position. Then he broke the horse into a run, charging directly at Jim.

Jim almost laughed. The man had lost his head. Either that, or else he had faced the fact that defeat and death were inescapable and had decided to go down fighting. At the same time, it was odd: and Jim had a sudden, reasonless memory flash of Smrgol, demanding of the other dragons in the cave: 'How many of you here would like to face just a single George in his shell, with his horn aimed at you?'

Then he and Sir Hugh came together with a crash, an unbelievable impact that in one blinding, pain-shot moment blotted out sight, thought, memory and all else . . . [6]

Sean laughed out loud. 'That would have been some collision,' and he glanced down at his watch. 'Jaysus, but I didn't realize how much time had gone by.' Then he held his hand out. 'Look, I'm a farmer and I've an early-morning start.'

'But I'm not finished telling Anne what she needs to know about draconic traditions,' Eppy protested, looking aggrieved at my having had two 'go's' at explanation.

'Well, maybe if Sean's interested enough, he'll come back for more tomorrow night?' I left my voice up and looked hopefully in my guest's direction.

'Well, now,' and Sean hesitated, forgetting in a brief moment that I was supposedly the querant, not himself. 'Well, yes, thank you very much, I would like to sit in again. That is, if it's not

'No, he's staying the night,' I said promptly, knowing that that inhibiting you?' He turned to me.

'No, no, glad to have you here. I'm always better with an audience,' I said, winking at Eppy who most certainly enjoyed an audience of any size.

He humphed. 'That is, if I'm *allowed* equal time.'

Sean smothered a laugh in a general 'good evening'. 'Do you need a lift home?'
was what Eppy must have in mind to have gone on so long in the first place.

I saw Sean out and locked up. Eppy was in the doorway, hands on hips.

'Now what's this all about anyway?'

'I don't know myself but he asked me to describe dragons to him.'

'That much I figured out for myself,' Eppy said in a sort of meditative way. 'Why?'

I did what Eppy often did: I put my finger alongside my nose and winked. 'That's for me to know and you to find out.'

'Ha!'

'Why should you mind? A warm house, decent food?'

'Who said I was staying?'

'I asked you to stay and you've never turned down bed, breakfast and dinner before. Besides I think he needs you more than me. And,' said I, pausing in sudden thought, 'I think you need to be here, too. To find out what his problem is. Right?'
Eppy *tried* to look indignant, secretive, surprised and irritated and failed in all four. 'You have an uncanny ability to turn up at the most serendipitous moments. I suspect you of ulterior motives and secret knowledge.'

'Me?'

'You don't fool me but I suspect I'll either figure it all out on my own or you'll vouchsafe for me the reasons in your own time. Either way, the guest room's all made up. Get a good night's sleep.'

'And you'll feed me in the morning?'

'Why not? I have to feed the cats.'

Second Session

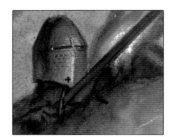

SEAN ARRIVED at precisely seven-thirty the next evening, trying to appear nonchalant. I wondered if he would come clean with his dragon problem because he had the air of a worried man. But, after courteous greetings, he settled himself in the same place which he had occupied last night and turned his head firmly toward Eppy.

Eppy cleared his throat. 'Shall I pick up where you left off last night, Anne?' he asked with some asperity.

'Please do,' and with a sweeping gesture of my arm, I settled back in my chair.

'*Other* dragonslayers benefited from the *original* George's example.' He gave me one more admonitory glance before he was off again in full spate. 'And not by any means were they all western or Christian. In Persia, for instance, Trita killed the primordial dragon, Ashi Dahaka. Faridun fought a fire-breathing dragon, and there were also Bahram Gur and the unfortunate King Ardashir who wasn't very successful and was eaten by a dragon. Perhaps the greatest of them was the epic hero Rustem, whose story is told in the *Shah Nameh* of Firdausi.

One dark night Rustem was travelling by himself in the wilderness, and lay down to sleep at night after finding pasture for his wonderful horse, Rukash. After a while, a horrible dragon emerged from the forest. It was eighty yards long, and so ferocious that not even elephants, lions, or desert demons dared venture near its cave. The dragon first attacked Rukash, who awakened Rustem with his whinnying. But when Rustem arrived, the dragon had vanished.

Rustem chided Rukash and went back to sleep. Once again, the dragon came out. Rukash raised the alarm, but once again, the ghastly worm vanished. The third time it approached, the faithful horse whinnied again and shredded the earth with its hoofs to rouse his master. Rustem sprang angrily to his feet, but, by then, there was just enough light for him to see the dreadful apparition that had so terrified Rukash.

Drawing his sword, Rustem closed on the dragon. He may well have been killed had not Rukash also attacked the monster with his flashing teeth and terrible hoofs.'

'Why, Rukash was just like Talat, Aerin's horse, I never realized that.'

Eppy glared at me for interrupting but I caught Sean's hastily erased smile.

As the dragon turned to slash at Rukash, Rustem sliced off its head, drenching the wilderness with its noxious blood.

King Gushtap was another notable dragon-slayer. His son, Prince Isfendiar, also killed a huge dragon by enclosing himself in a closed carriage which he had studded with sword blades, knives, spear-points, and other sharpened pricks and points.

When he had the carriage drawn to the dragon's lair, the immense serpent seized it in its cavernous maw, Isfendiar and all, and tried to gulp it down. But the pricks caught in its throat and choked it. Leaping from the carriage, Isfendiar thrust his sword deep into the dragon's brain. The flood of venom released almost killed the Prince, as it did many a dragonslayer. Fortunately, he recovered and, like Rustem, went on to perform many other heroic feats.

Eppy pointed to his now empty coffee cup and I dutifully rose to get refills for all of us. Talking dragons is thirsty work, even when you're not allowed to talk much yourself. As I went to the fridge for milk, I listened as the lecture continued.

'Northern dragons are not as charming and playful as their southern cousins,' the *Seannachie Brendan* said. 'And the stories don't always end well. In Norse myth, Nidhoggr, the "Dread Biter" or Midgard Orm, lies coiled among the roots of the great world-tree, Yggdrasil, either gnawing its own tail or slowly undermining the order of the world, as it awaits the final confrontation with Odin and the other gods in the Battle of Ragnarök.

You see, at the very beginning of time there was as yet no land or sea or sky, but only a world of endless cold and dark ruled over by the goddess Hel. It was called Niflheim, out of which twelve rivers flowed from the central spring Hvergelmir. The rivers froze as they emerged, and piled up in Ginnungagap, a glacial realm of ice, frost, sleet, and storm winds.

'Drops of venom frozen in Niflheim's rivers, collected until the giant Aurgelmir was formed. Then sparks and a hot wind from a fiery region to the south fell upon the ice pack, melting it sufficiently for Aurgelmir, the ancestor of the evil Frost Giants, to come forth.

'After his appearance, the Wonder Cow Audumla appeared from the ice and nourished Aurgelmir with her milk. And as she licked salt from the ice, she uncovered Buri, the ancestor of the gods.

'Borr, Buri's son, somehow has three sons, the greatest of whom is Odin. Odin and his brothers fight and kill Aurgelmir, and then fashion the world out of his corpse. His body becomes earth, his blood the sea, and his skull the sky, and so on with his eyes, hair, and other body parts. In this way, Borr's sons create Midgard or Middle-Earth, the human world.

There is great enmity between the gods and the forces of darkness, which include the terrible wolf Fenris. The dragon Nidhoggr is the final character in this happy family drama. Thor's sworn enemy, and the symbol of cosmic death and destruction, the ancient serpent narrowly escapes when old Hammerhead catches him on a hook baited with the head of an ox. But the wily dragon dives to the bottom of the ocean, where he lies curled in the roots of Yggdrasil around the base of Midgard.

The gods and Frost Giants war constantly with each other, although the finale is projected into the future, where on the field of Ragnarök they wipe each other out. There the Wolf, Fenris, swallows Odin, but the king of the gods is avenged by his son, Vidar, who tears the terrible beast apart. Garm, the demon-dog, and Tyr kill each other. So do Heimdall and the turncoat, Loki. And Thor faces the Midgard-Orm again and succeeds in killing it, but dies himself from exposure to the serpent's venom. Only Vidar and Thor's two sons survive the final slaughter.

'The twilight of the gods?' I asked.

'More like midnight. Depressing lot, those old Norsemen,' said Eppy.

'Spending the winter in Iceland would make anyone cross,' Sean said. 'Once I was storm-bound in Reykjavik for a couple of days. Not exactly my idea of holiday fun.'

'Hoard . . .' and once again Sean tensed with interest, fixing his eyes on Eppy who was unflappable, '. . . dragons were important to the northerners. Fafnir, a shape-shifting dragon, plays an important role in the story of Sigurd (or Siegfried as he is called in the German versions). And Beowulf, who was originally a Jutish hero, meets his doom from the injuries and venom he receives in his attack on a savage dragon threatening the peace of his realm.

'Some dragons, you know, are – were – creatures; men or women who turn into dragons at will or because they have been cursed.'

'You mean like a . . . a *werewolf*?'

'Yes, like Fafnir or even poor Melusine. They are often the most dangerous of all, because evil humans add cunning and

avarice to the dragon's wisdom and fierce protectiveness. Take Fafnir, for example. His story is part of the *Volsung Saga*, which Richard Wagner set to music in one of the greatest works of art the world has ever seen.'

'I may have slept through that one,' Sean said quietly.

Originally, Fafnir was one of the giants, for those were the days when the gods of Asgard still walked in Middle Earth. He stole the golden treasure of Andvari, the Dwarf, which contained the Ring of the Niebelungs. And because he sought to protect the hoard and also because of the curse that Andvari had laid on anyone who possessed it, Fafnir was transformed into a huge, vicious, and clever dragon.

Fafnir's brother, Reginn, also coveted the treasure and plotted for years to wrest it away. He found his chance in a young child, Sigurd the Volsung or Siegfried. The last of his race, Sigurd-Siegfried had been entrusted to Reginn to foster. But Reginn's heart was corrupted by greed, and he reared the boy to be honest, trusting, and fearless only as part of his evil scheme.

When Sigurd had grown to young manhood, Reginn told him about Fafnir and the treasure and the terrible fear that prevented anyone from challenging the dragon for it.

'I will do it!' Sigurd swore. 'But you must first make me an unbreakable sword to plunge into the dragon's heart.'

Twice Reginn forged a sword and twice it shattered when Sigurd tested it. Finally, the youth obtained from his mother the halves of the sword Gram that had belonged to his father, Sigmund, the son of Volsung. These Reginn forged anew into a sword so strong it split the very anvil on which it was made.

So Reginn led Sigurd to the dragon's lair on Gnita Heath and pointed out the track Fafnir followed each morning when he went to the stream to drink.

'Big fellow,' Sigurd observed from the size of the track.

'You may kill him, even so,' Reginn answered, 'if you dig a hole in the dragon's path and stab him to the heart as he passes above you on his way to the river.'

'But if his blood gushes over me, won't it poison me?' asked Sigurd.

'There's no use offering you advice,' Reginn replied, 'if you fear every little danger.'

'I fear nothing,' Sigurd said and started towards the cave. But Reginn found a hiding place among the rocks by the river, for he greatly feared the dragon.

Sigurd began to dig a pit in the dragon's path. But an old man came up to him and asked what he was doing. He had a staff, a cloak, and a long, white beard, and only one eye showed under his broad-brimmed hat.

Sigurd told him of Reginn's plan.

'You are following the advice of someone who wishes you harm,' the old man said. 'Reginn plans for you to kill the dragon but die in the battle so he can have the treasure. Dig a deep pit but add a shallow trench to the side of it. Then lie in the trench while the dragon's blood falls into the pit after you stab him.'

Then the old man vanished, and Sigurd realized that he had been speaking to Odin, king of the gods of Asgard. For he had once been told that, disguised as an old one-eyed wanderer, Odin visited those he wished to help.

So Sigurd dug the deep pit and the shallow trench, and lay there in wait for Fafnir. He was not frightened by the roaring of the dragon nor of the venom dripping from its jaws. And, as the dragon passed over the pit, he thrust his sword under its left shoulder, deep into its heart. Then he quickly withdrew it and in the same movement flung himself into the shallow trench.

Aware that he had received a death-wound, Fafnir lashed out with his teeth and tail. Everything within reach was smashed to bits. Then he lay still and cried with a human voice, 'What mighty hero has killed me? What brave son of a famous father is so bold as to come against me with a sword?'

'My race is unknown to mortal men,' Sigurd answered. 'They call me a noble beast.'

'Reginn, my brother, has done this,' Fafnir said. 'For I was a man even as he is until I robbed Andvari of his gold and the magic ring. But I know his plans. You are Sigurd the Volsung who shall be called Fafnirsbane

because you have killed me. You may take my Hoard, but remember that it will be the bane of all who possess it just as it was mine. For the Curse of Andvari is still on it.'

'Hoards aren't always cursed, are they?' Sean asked in such a nervous tone of voice that Eppy regarded him with surprise.

'Not always . . . But we'll talk about that later . . . Then Fafnir turned on his side and died. Even so, he did not regain his human form, but remained a dragon.

Afterwards Reginn approached and clapped Sigurd on the back. 'Hail, mighty hero! You have won a splendid victory. Yet the dragon was once my brother, and I am partly guilty of his murder. But I will take the full guilt of his death upon myself. Cut out the dragon's heart, roast it and give it to me to eat. Thus, there will be no blood-feud between our kin.'

So Sigurd cut out Fafnir's heart and began roasting it over the fire. After a while he touched the meat to see if it was cooked. The gravy burned his finger and he quickly licked it off. But the moment the heart's-blood of the dragon touched his tongue, he began to understand the speech of the birds in the nearby trees.

'There sits stupid Sigurd,' said the woodpecker, 'roasting the dragon's heart for someone else to eat. If he ate it himself he would become the wisest and the most blessed of men. For we could tell him how to awaken the lady Brynhild, Odin's daughter, from her magic sleep and win her for his wife – and how to become a great king as well.'

'And there sits Reginn,' said another woodpecker, 'planning to murder Sigurd and steal Andvari's Hoard. And if Reginn eats the dragon's heart, what is to stop him from winning Brynhild, too?'

A third bird asked, 'Why does Sigurd not strike off that traitor Reginn's head and keep Andvari's Hoard for himself?'

'Why not indeed?' Sigurd shouted and leaped to his feet.

In a flash he struck off Reginn's head with the sword Gram. Then he made his supper of the dragon's heart and spent the night in the cave, sleeping upon Andvari's Hoard, which Fafnir had guarded for so many years. And the following morning, guided by the birds, Sigurd the Volsung set out to win Brynhild as his wife. But that is another story.

'What about some supper, boys?' I asked because I could hear someone's stomach rumbling. Eppy's, I suspected, but Sean perked up, too. Well, maybe he hadn't had much at home in order to get here on time.

First Meal Break

A QUICK SPANISH omelette and toast was consumed by all three of us. Eppy looked quite revived and ready for more.

'Do dragons always get killed?' asked Sean.

'Not by any means,' Eppy said. 'A number of heroes get killed by the dragon, even if the dragon himself dies. Beowulf is one of the most famous.

'Every school child knows that Beowulf earns undying fame in his fight with the monster, Grendel, and his even more terrible mother. He even becomes king of his people, the Geats. But few remember that he met his death fifty years later killing a huge dragon who was furiously protecting his hoard.'

'Remind us,' Sean said with a worried glance in my direction.

'Here, at last, is your true medieval dragon; a monster of chaos and mortal threat, some fifty feet long, bat-winged, and fully fire-breathing. He lives in a tomb on a rocky point surrounded by the sea, in the very heart of death. There he guards an immense hoard of treasure, the very model of the jealous, vengeful serpent.

'This part of the poem begins when one of Beowulf's warriors seeks refuge in a burial cave during an encounter with a band of foes. Deep within he finds a mound of gold and jewels, engraved bowls and plates, jewelled brooches, girdles and combs, gleaming helmets, bright swords and shields. But the horrified thane sees a huge dragon asleep atop it all, wisps of smoke trailing from his flaring nostrils.

'For a fatal moment, greed overcomes terror, and like Jason, Indra, Zeus, and even Bilbo Baggins of *The Hobbit* fame, the thane snatches up as much of the hoard as he can carry.'

I'd been watching Sean intently and now I saw him swallow. So, he had a dragon and/or a dragon's hoard. Did he need to know *how* to get rid of the family dragon? I was tickled at this possibility but, despite what Eppy had said about there being Irish dragons, I didn't actually think that's what Sean's was.

Eppy's voice rolled on. 'Once safely home, he buries most of it, but takes one golden goblet to Beowulf, claiming that he had found it.

'Soon, however, disaster befalls the Geats. The dragon awakens

45

and immediately realizes that his hoard has been disturbed, for he knows each piece by sight. Roaring furiously, he springs out of the cave, finds the warrior's footprints, and sets out to wreak havoc on the thief.'

Sean was hanging on Eppy's every word now, leaning forward with elbows on his knees and his mouth slightly open, listening intently.

He sweeps over the bright dwellings of the Geats, pouring fire upon them from the night sky. In terror, the people send word to Beowulf, who now understands where the goblet has come from, and the dire consequences of its theft. Even were it possible to return the stolen treasure, he also knows that once disturbed, the enraged dragon will never leave his people in peace.

The old king orders his armourers to forge a great shield of iron. Then he dons his helmet and corselet, girds on his mighty sword Naegling and his battle-knife, and summons his warrior band.

'I go alone to fight the dragon,' he declares. 'But I vow not to take one step backwards once I raise my sword. Where we meet, there will I fight to the death.'

Then Beowulf sets out for the cave. His warriors follow him, but remain at a safe distance to watch the battle. Beowulf climbs to the tomb's rocky entrance to meet the dragon, shouting defiance. Out of the cave pour flames, the battle-breath of the monster. Then the fell dragon emerges, his tail lashing in rage.

Taking his ancient battle-sword in hand and holding his shield before him, Beowulf charges. As the flames curl round him, he strikes the dreadful serpent so hard that Naegling bites to the bone. The dragon puts up a terrific fight, of course.

'Of course,' Sean echoed glumly.

'Unfortunately, Beowulf is an old man by now, and starts to get the worse of it. As the dragon spews out deadly war-flames, Beowulf is ringed round with fire. His warrior band all flee, except for young Wiglaf, Beowulf's kinsman, and the last of his house. Although untried in battle, he bears his father's wondrous sword, forged by giants and victorious in many battles.

'Let us help our valiant king while the fierce flame still flares,' he cries. 'Before God I would think it a shameful deed if any of us should bear our shields back to our homes if we fail to fell the foe and save the Lord of the Geats.'

He then charges through the baneful smoke to the side of his king. 'Beowulf, beloved Lord,' he shouts encouragingly, 'triumph in this battle, as in the days of your youth you swore to win fame while your breath lasted. Now guard your life with all your strength, and I will aid you!'

Once again, the dragon rages toward them, flashing flame. Wiglaf's shield shrivels in the blast until only the rim remains. But he fights on, sheltering behind Beowulf's great iron shield.

Again Beowulf swings his battle-sword with all his strength. But the ancient blade shatters. And for the third time, the monstrous dragon rushes on the king. Fierce and flaming, he fastens his fangs in Beowulf's throat. The king's life-blood streams from the welling wound.

But brave Wiglaf lashes out with his sword, plunging it into the dragon's side, mortally wounding it. Beowulf, now near death from his poisoned wound, draws his battle knife and thrusts it deep into the dragon's belly.

With a great shriek, the terrible worm thrashes and dies. Beowulf then cuts the monster into two parts and casts them into the sea.

But this is the last victory of Beowulf, the mighty warrior, the end of his work in this world. His wound burns and swells as the venom works in his body. He sinks to a rock near the cave and summons Wiglaf to his side.

'My death is at hand. I give thanks to the King of Glory, the Eternal Lord, for all the great treasure that I have won for my people on this my death-day. Spend it well, for the good of my people, you who must guard them now.'

Then Beowulf gives his ring and helmet to Wiglaf. 'Use them well. For you are the last of our line. You are now the guardian of the Geats.'

Such were Beowulf's last words. As he spoke them his soul passed from his breast to seek the glory of Heaven.

'Not exactly a happy ending,' Sean said.

'You seem interested in a hoard story, though,' I remarked.

'I think I'm beginning to prefer maidens.'

'Very well, then,' said Eppy, 'here is Gottfried von Strassburg's classic story of a dragon, a hero, and a maiden.'

When Arthur was king in Britain, there was a young knight of Cornwall named Tristan of Lyonesse, the nephew of King Mark. He had gained renown by defeating in single combat Sir Marhault, champion of Gorman, King of Ireland, thus freeing Cornwall from paying a cruel tribute each year of youths and maidens.

But Tristan was wounded in the fray. And as Marhault's sword was poisoned, the wound could not be cured until he went disguised as the minstrel Tantris to the court of King Gorman whose wife, Queen Isaud, Marhault's sister, was skilled in the arts of healing. After he was restored to health, Tantris stayed on as a welcome guest, for he could play the harp and sing more sweetly than any minstrel in Ireland.

When he returned at last to the court of his uncle, he told especially of the beauty of Iseult the Fair, daughter of King Gorman and Queen Isaud. King Mark took council with his lords and said, 'King Gorman has no other child. Would it not profit both our lands if I secured a lasting peace by taking the fair Iseult to be my wife and the Queen of Cornwall?'

'But how can this come to pass?' they asked. 'The King and Queen of Ireland hate us for the slaying of Marhault and the ending of the tribute.'

'Uncle,' said Tristan, 'let me undertake this quest. For I have been to Ireland and won the friendship of the fair Iseult and Queen Isaud, who cured me of my wound, even though they had vowed deadly vengeance on Tristan of Lyonesse!'

So Tristan set out in a small ship and came to Ireland. The next morning he rose before dawn and armed himself secretly. Taking his strongest spear, he mounted his steed and rode forth into the wilderness.

He rode till the sun was high overhead, then turned into a valley where the dragon had its lair. Afar off, he saw three men galloping over the moor. A fourth followed them some way behind, so as not to be seen. This was the Steward of King Gorman, who would have wed the Princess Iseult. But she despised him for a coward and a braggart. For whenever knights rode forth bent on adventure, the steward accompanied them only so that men might say they had seen him ride forth. For he would never face the dragon, but always returned swifter than he went out.

Presently Tristan heard a terrible roar, and the cries of men in mortal anguish. Then the man who had followed the three knights came galloping back the way he had come, spurring his horse ever faster. Tristan thought no more of him, but rode down into the valley. Ere long he saw the dragon advancing towards him, spewing smoke and flame.

The knight laid his spear in rest, and set spurs to his steed, and rode so swiftly, and struck so strongly, that the spear entered the open jaws, and pierced through the throat right into the dragon's heart. But Tristan had hurled himself with such force against the dragon that his horse fell dead, and he could scarcely free himself from the steed. The vile serpent fell upon the corpse and partly devoured it, till the wound from Tristan's spear pained it so greatly that it left the horse half-eaten, and fled into a rocky ravine.

Tristan pursued the dragon, which fled before him, roaring for pain till the rocks rang. It spat fire from its jaws and tore the earth, till the pain of the wound overcame it, and it crouched down under a wall of rock. Then Tristan drew his sword, hoping to slay the creature easily, but it was a hard strife, the hardest Tristan had ever fought. In truth he thought it would be his death. For the dragon possessed teeth and claws sharper than a shearing knife, as well as smoke and flame. Often Tristan had to find shelter behind trees and bushes, for the fight was so fierce that his shield was seared to a cinder.

But the conflict did not endure much longer, for the spear in the dragon's vitals began to pain him so sharply that he lay on the ground, rolling over and over in agony. Then Tristan struck with his sword at the heart of the monster. The blade went in right to the hilt, and the dragon gave forth a roar so grim and terrible that it sounded as if earth and sky fell together, and the cry was heard far and wide through the land.

Tristan himself was terrified. But when he saw the beast was dead, he went near and forced the jaws open, and cut out the tongue. Then he closed the jaws again, and put the tongue in his pouch. He turned again to the moor, thinking to rest through the day and return to his ship secretly by night. But he was exhausted by the stress of the fight and the fiery breath of the dragon. Seeing a pond close by into which a clear stream flowed from the rock, he made towards it. As he came to the cool waters the weight of his armour and the venom of the dragon's tongue overpowered him, and he fell senseless by the stream.

Meanwhile the Steward heard the death-cry of the dragon as he rode homeward.

51

'Someone has killed or wounded the dragon mortally,' he thought. 'With cunning and luck I may still win the fair Iseult!'

He returned the way he had fled, and presently found the remains of Tristan's steed. At this he paused, shaking with fear. But hearing no sound, he rode carefully along the track to the dragon's cave and came upon the great serpent lying dead.

When he was sure that the dragon was really dead, he laughed and clapped his hands for joy. He sprang on his horse and charged the dead dragon with his spear, breaking off the handle in the wound. He dismounted and taking his sword, cut and hacked the carcase. Had he been able, he would have cut off its head, but this was beyond his strength.

Then he searched for the knight who had in truth killed the dragon, for he knew that he must be lying wounded nearby and would have killed him as well so that he could not gainsay his false account. But he did not find Tristan, and at last gave up the search and set out for home.

When he arrived at the castle, he told everyone how he had slain the dragon and sent out a wagon to bring back the head. 'Another man was there before me,' he said. 'I do not know who he was, but he met with an evil end before I arrived. For the dragon devoured both him and his horse, which you may still see there, half-eaten. But I have dared more than any man before me, and tomorrow I shall claim as my reward the hand of the fair Iseult to be my wife now, and the Kingdom of Ireland after her father's death.'

When Iseult the Fair heard of the Steward's deed, she said to her mother: 'Rather than marry him, I will slay myself!'

'It has not yet come to that,' Queen Isaud replied. 'For I do not believe that the Steward killed the dragon. And tonight we will discover what truly happened.'

When it was dark, Iseult and her mother went secretly to the moor and found the dragon dead, with the Steward's spear broken off in its side, and its head hacked off and carried away.

'He who had fought and slain the dragon would seek water,' said Queen Isaud. And shortly they came upon Tristan lying senseless beside the spring.

'Now here is a wonder,' she cried. 'This is the minstrel Tantris who stayed with us last year. But now he wears the armour of a knight. And I cannot read his coat of arms, for the shield is all melted from the dragon's breath.'

They had Tristan carried back to the castle, where Queen Isaud applied her skills so well that before morning he was well-nigh restored from the dragon's venom and able to tell them the tale.

'But why did you come secretly, clad as a knight, to slay the dragon?' asked Queen Isaud.

Then Tristan told them the whole truth – how he was their sworn enemy who had slain Sir Marhault, and how he had returned to be healed and then come to win Iseult to be the bride of King Mark.

'No better lot could be hers,' said Queen Isaud. 'Therefore, Sir Tristan of Lyonesse, if you save Iseult from the Steward, we will forgive you my brother's death and honour you as our true friend and preserver. Moreover, you shall take Iseult to be the bride of your uncle with our blessing.'

The next day, when high noon had come, a great gathering met before the castle. But there was much murmuring among the crowd, for few believed that the Steward had indeed killed the dragon, and none wished him to marry Iseult and be their king in days to come.

When the King and Queen had taken their places, the Steward stepped forward and said, 'Your Majesties, I have slain the dragon. Here is its head to prove my words. And all these men can bear witness that they saw the dragon dying from the wounds I gave it. See! here is my spear still in its brain.'

Then Tristan rose and said, 'Lords all, mark this marvel. For I slew the dragon and this man afterwards smote it a second time to death!'

'No, Sire, I killed it,' insisted the Steward. 'And this head proves my words.'

'My Lord King,' said Tristan, 'since he brings the head as proof, and swears that it was struck off by those who saw the dragon die, bid him look within the jaws. If the tongue be there, I withdraw my claim.'

They opened the jaws, but found nothing there. As they stood amazed, Sir Tristan withdrew the tongue from his pouch and said, 'See if this is the dragon's tongue or not.'

They looked, and saw that it was indeed the tongue. And all cheered, except the Steward who stood there knowing neither what to say nor whither to run.

'If you doubt my word and this proof, Sir Steward,' said Tristan, 'then your course is clear. We fight to the death in single combat.'

But the steward was afraid to fight. He made his excuses, and left the castle in haste, and was never seen again.

'Sir Tristan of Lyonesse,' said King Gorman, 'you have won my daughter and with her the kingdom after my death. For no man can have any doubt that you killed the dragon!'

'Most noble king,' said Tristan. 'I came to Ireland to win the fair Iseult for my uncle, King Mark, and I would be shamed forever if I took her for myself after having won her.'

So Iseult set out with Brangwin, her maid, in Sir Tristan's ship and in due course was wed to King Mark, although she loved Sir Tristan, and he loved her. But the sad end of that love is another story.

'As I recall, there were quite a lot of dragons around Arthur's time,' I said.

'A plague of them. Dragons were also featured prominently in Scandinavian and Anglo-Saxon artwork of the Dark Ages, such as the Sutton Hoo burial cache dug up in Suffolk about fifty years back.

'According to Sir Thomas Malory's account, one year at Pentecost, a hermit came to Camelot and was shown the Siege Perilous at the Round Table,' Eppy began.

'And who is to sit there?' he asked.

'No man except the best and purest knights in the world," said King Arthur and all his knights. 'Yet we do not know who he may be.'

'You speak the truth,' the hermit replied, 'for he is not yet born. But, before this day next year, the knight shall be born who will sit in the Siege Perilous and achieve the Quest of the Holy Grail.'

With these words, the hermit turned and departed suddenly from their sight. After the feast, Sir Lancelot rose as if guided by some mysterious force, girded on his armour, took his shield and spear in hand, and set out in quest of adventure.

After a while he crossed over the Bridge of Corbyn. In the distance he glimpsed the fairest tower he had ever seen. Beneath it was a pretty little town full of people. When the people saw him coming, men and women all at once cried to him, 'Welcome, Sir Lancelot the flower of knighthood! For you shall help us out of our troubles.'

'What do you mean with this appeal to me?' asked Sir Lancelot.

'Fair knight,' they answered, 'within this tower there is a dolorous lady who has dwelled there in pain for a long time. And we know that you, Sir Lancelot, shall deliver her.'

Her name, they said, was Elaine, daughter to the King of that land, Pelles.

Without more ado, they led Lancelot into the tower. And when he came to the chamber where the lady was, the iron doors unlocked themselves and flew open before him. The chamber he entered was as hot as an oven. And there he found as fair a lady as ever he saw. By the wicked enchantments of the jealous witch, Morgan le Fay, she had been imprisoned there for five years because the people had called her the fairest lady in the land. And she could not leave until the bravest knight in the world took her by the hand.

So Lancelot led her forth by the hand. And, when she was arrayed again Lancelot thought that she was indeed the fairest lady he had ever seen, saving only Queen Guinevere.

Then the lady said to Lancelot: 'Sir, if it please you, come with me to the chapel close by to give thanks to God, and thus to complete your quest.'

When they came to the chapel they knelt together and all the people knelt also and gave thanks for the lady's deliverance. But when they said to him, 'Sir knight, since you have delivered the lady, you must also deliver us from the terrible dragon which dwells yonder in the tomb.'

Then Sir Lancelot took his sword and shield, and said, 'Take me there. And I will accomplish for you what God gives me strength to do.'

They led him to a great flat tomb. The stone laid on it had these words cut into it in letters of gold: 'There shall come a Leopard of royal blood and he shall slay this dragon. And the Leopard shall become the father of a Lion. And the Lion shall surpass all other Knights in the world.'

When the lid was lifted from the tomb, out leaped a horrible and fiendish dragon spitting wild fire from his jaws. Sir Lancelot drew his sword and fought both long and fiercely. But at long last, with great pain and difficulty, Sir Lancelot slew the dragon.

Thereafter came King Pelles and saluted him.

'Now, fair knight,' he said, 'what is your name? By your knighthood, I require you to tell me.'

'Majesty,' he replied, 'I am Sir Lancelot of the Lake.'

'And my name is Pelles,' the king said, 'descended from Joseph of Arimathea, in whose sepulchre Our Lord Jesus was laid after the Crucifixion.'

They embraced warmly and then went into the hall and sat down to dine. Shortly thereafter a Dove flew through the window carrying in her mouth a little censor of gold. At once the air was filled with a scent so sweet that it seemed as if all the spices in the world were there. And suddenly they found before them on the table all such meats and drinks as they would desire.

Then a fair young maiden came into the hall carrying a Vessel of gold in her hands. King Pelles knelt himself down devoutly and said a prayer, and all the company did likewise.

'In God's Name, what does this mean?' asked Lancelot.

'Sir Knight,' King Pelles answered, 'this is the most wonderful sight that anyone may look on in this world. When it comes to Camelot, the Round Table will be empty for a season. For it is the Holy Grail, the Cup from which Jesus and his disciples drank at the Last Supper and which Joseph of Arimathea brought to this land.'

Lancelot remained in the castle for many days. For King Pelles knew that the appointed time had come. Lancelot, who had slain the dragon, would become the father of Galahad, the best and purest knight of all. Only he would complete the Quest of the Holy Grail and sit in the Siege Perilous at Camelot. And the fair Elaine was destined to be the mother of Galahad.

And so, in time, it came to pass. But how that happened and what came of it is another story.'

'At least that dragon didn't have a hoard,' Sean said with visible relief. 'Are medieval dragons always so evil and dangerous?'

'Not always,' Eppy replied. 'Sometimes, they are even noble, or at least tragic victims of fate.

'For instance, in the beautiful illuminated Prayer Book of the Duc du Berry, there is a lovely miniature of the Castle of Lusignan. Far in the distance, you can just make out a golden dragon flying around a high tower. The Romance of Melusine tells the tale of that dragon.'

One day, Count Raymond of Poitou was hunting in the forest when he came upon a beautiful maiden at the Fountain of Thirst, which was sacred to the People of Faerie. The young man fell deeply in love with her and asked her to marry him. Her name, she said, was Melusine. She was one of three daughters of the King Elinas of Scotland and the nymph, Pressina.

Her mother had married Elinas under the sole condition that he never visit her during her confinement before giving birth. But he was so overjoyed when his daughters were born that he forgot his promise and rushed to her side. In a flash, Pressina and her babies were transported to an island off the coast of Scotland. From there, they could see Elinas' kingdom. But Pressina explained each day to her children they could never visit there because of their father's broken promise.

Years later, Melusine got her revenge by entombing Elinas under Mount Brandelois. Furious, Pressina placed Melusine under a terrible spell. Until she met a man who would marry her on condition that he never see her on a Saturday, once every month she would turn into a dragon from the waist down.

Raymond was so smitten that he gave his word without a second thought. The young couple were married and lived happily enough at the beautiful castle of Lusignan, which Melusine built by magic. Their only sorrow was that each of their children was born with some bodily or spiritual deformity. Still, Raymond kept his promise faithfully until one day, a cousin told him that Melusine really had a demon lover who came to her on Saturdays.

The following Saturday, Raymond hid behind a tapestry, from where he saw his beloved wife emerge from her bath in her half-dragon form. Still, he kept her secret. But now he understood why their children had been cursed.

Then one day, in a fit of anger, Raymond shouted at her, 'Go from me, you vile serpent! You have corrupted my entire family!'

Melusine was overwhelmed with grief. She announced that from that day until the Castle of Lusignan fell into ruin, she would be condemned to fly through the air in the form of a golden dragon. Moreover, she would appear to bewail the imminent death of each Count of Lusignan. And so it came to pass until the very day the castle burned to the ground.

'Some medieval dragons don't eat anyone and some don't even get skewered. Take, for instance, the tale of Lludd and Llewelys in the great Welsh epic, the *Mabinogi*.'

In olden times, when Lludd was king in Britain, on every May Eve, a terrible cry echoed throughout the whole island. It was so loud, milk curdled in the pail and eggs were shattered in the nest. No one could sleep.

Lludd travelled to France to consult his brother, King Llewelys, who was something of a wizard. Llewelys told Lludd that the scream came from a great red dragon under attack by another dragon, a white one from afar.

On his return, Lludd had the whole of Britain measured to determine the exact centre, which was found, of course, at Oxford.

'Of course,' Sean and I said in unison.

'So Lludd had a pit dug there,' Eppy went on, eyeing us suspiciously. 'He then had a great cauldron placed in it, filled with the best mead, and covered with linen. Soon the dragons appeared, weary of fighting and eager for a bit of liquid refreshment. Falling to the bottom of the cauldron, they drank all the mead, then understandably fell into a deep sleep.

'Lludd and his men wrapped the dormant dragons in the linen and took them to a distant hill in the west, Dinas Ffaraon – later called Dinas Emrys, as we shall see. There they placed them in a wooden chest which was then buried deep in the hill and covered with great slabs of stone. Thus the terrible shriek was ended.

'Centuries later, according to the accounts in Geoffrey of Monmouth's *History of the Kings of Britain* and Robert Wace's *Roman de Brut*, the two dragons are released by Merlin, who was trying to save his own life from the Vortigern, the ill-advised king who invited Hengist and Horsa, the Jute warriors, to Britain as his allies. In constructing a fortress atop a tall hill in north Wales, this bloody-minded king had been frustrated by the disappearance of materials each night. His advisors claimed that only the sacrifice of a child without a human father would still the earth.

'Searching for such a child, Vortigern's soldiers overhear children taunting a boy for being fatherless and likely sired by the devil himself. But Emrys or Merlin (as he turns out to be) dissuades Vortigern from murdering him by accurately predicting that the hill is disturbed by two dragons fighting at the bottom of a subterranean lake.

'He is laughed to scorn by the king's druids. But when the lake is drained and the dragons are released, the foundations are secured, along with Merlin's place in mythical and literary history.

'You see, for the sixth-century British Christians fighting to preserve their nation from the heathen Saxons on one side and Irish pirates and Picts on the other, the red dragon of Rome represented law, order, and civilization. It was immortalized in the royal crest of Great Britain and still flies proudly on the flag of Wales. It is the only country in the world other than Bhutan, you know, that has a dragon on its flag.'

'No, I didn't.' Sean was beginning to sound impatient.

'And why both Uther and Arthur were known as Pendragon,' Eppy concluded.

'Actually,' I began, 'there are cases where dragons and humans are fighting on the same side.'

'There are?' Eppy said, deliberately egging me on in his droll fashion.

'Yes,' and I reached for the appropriate book of the Sunrunners' series.

'What the dragons began, humans must finish.'

Although the Vellant'im no longer fell on their knees or ran in terror at the sight of the huge beasts, Riyan had been essentially correct . . . : a flight of them sweeping through the sky, blotting out the moonlight, could make the bravest of the enemy shudder. Pol would have been terrified himself if he hadn't known the three dragons were on his side.

He didn't last long in the thick of it. The agony in his head, helped by Kazander's noxious potion only enough so he could ride and fight, came back in force when a bearded warrior on a Radzyn mare knocked the side of his helm with the flat of a sword. He didn't fall from the saddle, but as he swayed drunkenly and scrabbled to right himself, he saw another sword gleam its silvery moon-lit way toward his belly.

Another sword countered it in a crash of steel.

'Kazander!' Maarken shouted. 'Get Pol out of here.'

'No – I . . .'

Groggy with pain, he heard Azhdeen scream overhead and looked up. Kazanader had his reins and was tugging his infuriated stallion out of the chaos. 'Stop it, damn you . . .'

'With respect, great and noble Azhrei, shut up!'

Pol spent the next little while wondering if he was going to faint. The indignity of the thought kept him sternly in his saddle: Azhdeen's next roar nearly startled him out of it.

The dragon flew toward him out of the moon, and though he was nothing but a blackness against the sky, Pol knew by the sound of his wing beats that he was hurt. Azhdeen landed a little way from him: he was already off his horse and racing toward the dragon.

A great shout went up from the Vellant'im. Pol barely heard it. He ran straight for the wing Azhdeen held out at an awkward angle, conjured a fingerflame so he could get a look at the silvery underskin.

'Oh, Goddess,' he breathed, seeing an arrow lodged in the flight muscles beside one long bone. There were other rents in the dragon's hide where arrows had scraped, pricking blood. Pol turned to look into Azhdeen's huge eyes and whispered, 'This will hurt. Hold still, I beg of you. It has to come out.' Gripping the arrow in both hands, he yanked it from the dragon's wing.

Azhdeen growled low in his throat and butted his head against Pol's backside. 'Just a little bit longer while I clean it,' Pol said, and unstoppered the water skin at his belt. He poured the whole of its contents over the wound. The dragon yelped once, then hummed as cool water soothed the gouge.

'That's better, isn't it?' Pol asked, smiling as he rubbed the delicate blue-grey hide between Azhdeen's eyes. The dragon rumbled, stretching his hurt wing. 'If you can fly on that, old son, get yourself up to the lake and I'll bring something later to make it heal . . .'

Azhdeen reared up to his full height, jaws parting in a deafening shriek. The injured wing swept forward to enclose Pol in a suffocating shimmer of silver hide. He pushed it away, gently, at first and then more insistently and saw a hundred and more Vellant'im bearing down on him, marching in closed ranks, their swords aloft like so many fluttering steel feathers polished by moonlight. Leading them was a white-garbed man who wore no gold in his beard, held no sword, whose lips moved in impassioned screams Pol's numbed ears could not hear.

Two things crossed his mind as he drew his sword: a piercing disappointment that it was not the High Warlord he faced, and a vicious glee of anticipation. He was about to kill these savages who had dared hurt his dragon.

They stopped just out of arrowshot when Azhdeen howled again. Pol heard it more as a vibration in the hollows of his body than against his sound-shocked ears. He laughed, seeing them hesitate.

'What are you waiting for?' he shouted, stepping from the shelter of the dragon's wing, unable to hear his own voice. 'If it's me you want, I'm here.'

The enemy advanced. Pol stood his ground, the dragon behind him. The one in white screamed in a frenzy of hate. Sunrunner's Fire sprang up in a circle around him, and Pol laughed as the Vellant'im stopped and

the man inside the flames turned and turned and flinched with every turning. Screaming differently now.

The sand below Pol's feet trembled. The moonlight and his own Fire showed scores of mounted soldiers, clean-shaven, angry faces intent on the enemy threatening their High Prince. Their Azhrei. Pol started forward, knowing he had done a clever thing without being aware of it. He had bought time for Maarken to gather a charge, and with that time he had bought his own life.

And then all was familiar insanity around him. Swordplay in the practice yard had a rhythm, an elegance, a mannered pattern to thrust and parry and counterthrust. Battle lurched like a broken plow drawn by a lame elk.

Pol glanced to his left, where he figured Azhdeen would have been into view by now. The dragon was stamping both hind legs in the sand, head thrown back as he howled again and again. Pol could almost hear him through the ringing in his ears. Azhdeen's huge spiked tail had skewered a Vellanti; he shook it to rid himself of the weight, and lashed it back and forth to discourage further vainglory. Pol laughed to himself at the sight, and returned his attention to the path he and Maarken were carving through the enemy forces.[7]

'And then, there are dragons fightings dragons,' I said.

'I thought we hadn't heard the last from you,' Eppy said, but he went to get himself more beers while I reached for Jane Yolen's *Dragonsblood*.

'It's eager.' The whisper ran around the crowd. They always liked that in young dragons. Time enough to grow cautious in the Pit. Older dragons often were reluctant and had to be prodded with sticks, behind the wings or in the tender underparts of the tail. The betters considered it a great fault. Jakkin heard the crowd's appreciation of the red (dragon) as he came up into the stands.

Then he leaned forward, hands on the seatback in front of him, and watched as his red circled the ring.

It held its head high and measured the size of the Pit, the height of the walls. It looked over the betters as if to count them, and an appreciative chuckle ran through the crowd. The red scratched into the sawdust several times, testing its depth.

Then with an explosion, Bottle O'Rum came through the dragonlock and landed with all four feet planted well beneath the level of the sawdust, his claws fastened immovably to the boards.

'Good stance,' shouted someone in the crowd, and the betting began anew.

The red gave a little flutter with its wings, a flapping that might indicate nervousness, and Jakkin thought of it: 'He is a naught. A Stander. But thy nails and wings are fresh. Do not be afraid. Remember thy training.' At that the little red's head went high and its neck scales glittered in the artificial sun of the pit.

'Watch that neck,' shouted a heckler. 'There's one that'll be blooded soon.'

'Too soon,' shouted another from across the stands at him.

Bottle O'Rum charged the inviting neck.

It was just as Jakkin hoped, for charging from the fighting stance is a clumsy manoeuvre at best. The claws must all be retracted simultaneously, or one would catch in the boards. And the younger the dragon the more brittle its claws. The orange might be seven fights older than the red, but it was not fully mature. As Rum charged, the nails on his front right claw, probably the unum, Jakkin thought, did catch in the floorboards, and it

splintered, causing him to falter for a second. The red shifted its position slightly. Instead of blooding the red on the vulnerable neck, Rum's charge brought him heading onto the younger dragon's chest plates, the hardest and slipperiest part of a fighting dragon's armour. The screech of tooth on scale sent winces through the crowd. Only Jakkin was ready, for it was a manoeuvre he had taught his dragon in the sands.

'Now!' he cried out and thought at once.

The young red needed no urging. It bent its neck around in a fast vicious slash, and blood spurted from behind the ears of Mekkle's Rum.

'First blood!' cried the crowd.

Bottle O'Rum roared with the bite, loud and piercing. It was too high up in the throat yet, but with surprising strength. Jakkin listened carefully, trying to judge. He had heard dragons roar at the Nursery in anger or fear or when Likkarn had blooded one of them for a customer intent on hearing the timbre before buying. To him the roar sounded as if it had all its power in the top tones and none that resonated. Perhaps he was wrong, but if his red could make this a long fight with the orange, it might impress this crowd.

He leaned over the rail. 'Away, away good Red,' he thought to his dragon and smiled when the red immediately wheeled and winged up from its blooded foe.

The orange dragon in the pit shook its head and its blood spattered over the walls and into the stands. Each place a drop touched burned with that glow peculiar to the acidic dragon's blood. The onlookers ducked.

The orange Rum stood up tall again and dug back into the dust.

'Another stand,' said the gray-leather man to Jakkin's right.

'Pah! That's all it knows,' said a dark-skinned offworlder beside him. 'That's how it won its three fights. Good stance, but that's all.'

The red dragon's leap back had taken it to the north side of the pit. When it saw that Bottle O'Rum had chosen to stand, it circled closer warily.

Jakkin thought at it, 'He's good in the stance. Do not force him there. Make him come to thee.'

The dragon's thoughts, as always, came back clearly to Jakkin, wordless but full of color and emotion. The red wanted to charge: the dragon it had blooded was waiting. The overwhelming urge was to carry the fight to the foe.

'No, my Red. Trust me. Be eager, but not foolish,' cautioned Jakkin, looking for an opening.

But the crowd, as eager as the young dragon, was communicating to it, too. The yells of the men, their thoughts of charging, overpowered Jakkin's single line of calm. The red started to move.

When he saw the red bunching for a charge, Rum solidified his stance. His shoulders went rigid with the strain. Jakkin knew that if his red dived at that standing rock, it could quite easily break a small bone in its neck . . .

'Steady, steady,' Jakkin said, aloud. Then he shouted and waved a hand. '*No*!'

The red had already started its dive, but the movement of Jakkin's hand and his shout were signals too powerful for it to ignore, and at the last possible moment it pulled to one side. As it passed, Rum slashed at it with gaping mouth and shredded its wingtip.

'Blood,' the crowd roared and waited for the red dragon to roar back.

Jakkin felt its confusion, and his head swam with the red of the dragon's blood as his dragon's thoughts came to him. He watched as it soared to the top of the building and scorched its wingtip in the artificial sun, cauterizing its wound. Then, still hovering, it opened its mouth for its first blooded roar.

There was no sound.

'A mute!' called a man from the stands. He spat angrily to one side. 'Never saw one before.'

A wit near him shouted back, 'Never heard one, either.'

The crowd laughed at this, and passed the quip around the stands.

But Jakkin only stared up at his red. 'A mute,' he thought at it. 'Oh, my poor Red. You are as powerless as I.'

His use of the distracting pronoun 'you' further confused the young dragon, and it began to circle downward in a disconsolate spiral, closer and closer to the waiting Rum, its mind a maelstrom of blacks and grays.

Jakkin realized his mistake in time. 'It does not matter,' he cried out in his mind. 'Even with no roar, even voiceless, thou wilt be great!' He said it with more conviction than he really felt. But it was enough for the red. It broke out of its spiral and hovered, its wings working evenly.

The manoeuvre, however, was so unexpected that the pit-wise Bottle O-Rum was bewildered. He came out of his stance with a splattering of dust and fewmets, stopped, then charged again. The red avoided him easily, landing on his back and raking the orange scales with its claws. That drew no blood, but it frightened the older dragon into a hindfoot rise. Balancing on his tail, Rum towered nearly three metres high, his front claws scoring the air, a single shot of fire streaking from his slits.

The red backwinged away from the flames and waited.

'Steady, steady,' thought Jakkin, in control again. He let his mind recall for them both the quiet sands and the cool night when they had practised against the reed shelter a game of charges and clawing. Then he repeated out loud, 'Steady, steady.'

The scream was Bottle O'Rum's, a triumphant roar as he stood over the red whose injured wing was pinioned beneath Rum's right claw.

Jakkin trembled, but he willed his focus onto the red, whose thoughts came tumbling back into his head now in a tangle of muted colors and whines. 'Never mind, my Red,' soothed Jakkin. 'Never mind the pain. Recall the time I stood upon thy wing and we played at the Great Upset. Recall it well, thou mighty fighter. Remember. Remember.'

The red stirred only slightly and made a flutter of its free wing. The crowd saw this as a gesture of submission. So did Rum, and through him, his master Mekkle. But Jakkin did not. He knew the red had listened well and understood. The game was not over yet. Pit fighting was not all brawn; how often the books said that. The best fighters, the ones who lasted for years, did not have to be big. They did not have to be overly strong. But they did have to be cunning gamesters, and it was this he had known about his red from the first – its love of play.

The fluttering of the unpinioned wing caught Bottle O'Rum's eye and the orange dragon turned toward it, relaxing his hold by a single nail.

The red fluttered its free wing again. Flutter and feint. It needed the orange's attention totally on that wing. Then its tail could do the silent stealing it had learned in the sands with Jakkin.

Bottle O'Rum followed the fluttering as though laughing for his own coming triumph. His dragon jaws opened slightly in a deadly grin. If Mekkle had been in the stands instead of below in the stalls, the trick might not have worked. But the orange dragon, intent on the fluttering wing, leaned his head way back and fully opened his jaws, readying for the winning stroke. He was unaware of what was going on behind him.

'Now!' shouted Jakkin in his mind, later realizing that the entire stands had roared the words with him. Only the crowd had been roaring for the wrong dragon.

The red's tail came around with a snap, as vicious and accurate as a driver's whip. It caught the orange on its injured ear and across one eye.

Rum screamed instead of roaring and let go of the red's wing. The red was up in an instant and leaped for Bottle O'Rum's throat.

One, two, and the ritual slashes were made. The orange throat coruscated with blood, and instantly Rum dropped to the ground.

Jakkin's dragon backed at once, slightly akilter because of the wound in its wing.

'Game to Jakkin's Red,' said the disembodied voice over the speaker.'[8]

'You'll notice,' Eppy said, leaning toward Sean and pointing at me over his shoulder, that this poor woman has to *read* her contributions out of the book.' He pointed to his domed skull. 'I have all mine here.'

'So, enlighten us further from memory,' I replied with amused forebearance.

'There are more than enough dragons here on Earth,' Eppy said with a sniff, 'to have no need to go out of this world to find examples.'

'I mentioned Azhdeen for another reason,' I said. 'He doesn't have to hoard: he *makes* the gold himself and the humans hoard it.' I gave Sean the wink and I could see my remark interested him. 'On Melanie Rawn's planet, the female seals her eggs in a cave. When the young ones hatch, they have to burn their way out. They also have to eat each other to sustain themselves, so only the best survive. But their shells are turned to gold by their fiery breath. That is, if it's dragon gold you want.'

'No, not exactly, I mean . . .' Sean floundered about a bit. 'I mean, what Eppy's saying is *very* interesting.'

'Then I'll continue,' Eppy said, at his loftiest. 'The Russians also have dragons. I am told by Slavic dracologists that the most constant element in folk tales features a dragon endowed with three, six, or nine heads. And sometimes even more. Like most wurrums, they carry off beautiful girls and devour people. Even the evil demon, Kashchei the Immortal, often takes on the appearance of a dragon.

'I heard an old story once involving several of them. It's called "Little Rolling-pea" '.

Once long ago in the land of Russia there lived a husband and wife who had no children. One day the wife took a bucket, went for water, and after drawing water, started home. All at once she saw a pea rolling along.

'It's a gift from God,' she thought to herself. So she picked it up and ate it.

A few months later she gave birth to a baby boy. So they called him Little Rolling-pea. He grew and grew, not by years, but by hours, like millet dough when leavened. The proud parents nursed him in a way that couldn't be improved upon, and soon sent him off to school. But what other children learned only in three or four years, he grasped in only one, and all the books they had there were not enough for him.

One day he came home from school and said to his parents, 'Thank my teachers, for already many of them have come to learn from me. But, thanks be to God, I now know more than they do.'

'Conceited little brat,' I suggested.

'He has more than a little in common with Sigurd or Siegfried,' Eppy conceded. 'But don't interrupt. It's a long enough story as it is.

So Little Rolling-pea went into the street to amuse himself. He found a

pin, which he brought to his parents. "Take this piece of iron to a smith," he said to his father. "Have him make me a mace weighing seven poods." Now a pood, you know, weighs thirty-six pounds.

His father said nothing, but thought, 'God has given us a child different from other folks. He has a middling wit, but he is making a fool of me. How can a seven-pood mace be made out of a pin?'

So his father drove to town, bought seven poods of iron, and gave them to a smith. The smith made a seven-pood mace, and he brought it home. Little Rolling-pea took it and threw it up into the clouds.

Some while later, he lay down with his right ear to the ground, and on rising up called his father, 'See what is whizzing and humming! My mace is falling to the ground.'

He caught the mace on his knee but it broke in half. Little Rolling-pea became angry. 'Father, why did you not have a mace made for me out of the iron I gave you? If you had done so, it would not have broken, but only bent. Here is the same iron pin for you. Go and get it made, but don't add any metal of your own.'

So the smith put the iron in the fire and beat it with hammers and pulled it. It grew and grew until he made a seven-pood mace.

Little Rolling-pea took the mace and prepared to go on a journey. As he travelled, a huge fellow stopped him. 'I salute you, Little Rolling-pea! Where are you going?'

'Who are you?' Little Rolling-pea asked him.

'I am the mighty hero Overturn-hill.'

'Will you be my comrade?' asked Little Rolling-pea.

He replied: 'I am at your service.'

They went on together. After a while, the mighty hero, Overturn-oak met them.

'God bless you, brothers!' he said. 'Good health to you! What manner of men are you?'

'Little Rolling-pea and Overturn-hill.'

'Whither are you going?'

'To a far-away city.'

'May I join your company?'

'You may,' said Little Rolling-pea.

So they went to the city, and made themselves known to the king.

'What manner of men are you?' he asked them.

'Mighty heroes!'

'Then is it in your power to deliver this city? A ravenous dragon is destroying our people. He must be slain.'

'Why would we call ourselves mighty heroes, if we could not slay him?' Little Rolling-pea said.

Midnight came, and they went up to a bridge over the river. Up came a six-headed dragon, who posted himself upon the bridge. Immediately the dragon's horse neighed, his falcon chattered, and his hound howled. The dragon gave his horse a blow on the head. 'Don't neigh, devil's carrion! Don't chatter, falcon! And you, hound, don't howl! For here is Little Rolling-pea. Come forth, Little Rolling-pea! Shall we fight or shall we try our strength?'

'Good youths travel not to try their strength,' Little Rolling-pea answered, 'but only to fight.'

The combat began. Little Rolling-pea and his comrades struck the dragon three blows on three of his heads. Seeing that he could not escape destruction, the dragon said, 'Well, brothers, it is only little Rolling-pea that troubles me. So I'll settle matters with you.'

The three comrades smashed the dragon's remaining heads. Then they took the dragon's horse to the stable, his falcon to the mews, and his hound to the kennel. And Little Rolling-pea cut out the tongues from all

six heads, placed them in his knapsack, but the headless trunk they cast into the river.

They returned to the king, and presented the tongues as certain proof.

'I see that you are mighty heroes and deliverers of the city,' the king said. 'If you wish to drink and eat, take all manner of beverages and victuals without money and without tax.'

And with joy the king issued a proclamation throughout the realm, that all the eating houses, inns, and small public houses were to be open for the mighty heroes.

Well, they went everywhere, drank, amused themselves, refreshed themselves, and enjoyed various honours.

Night came, and exactly at midnight they went across the rosewood bridge. All at once, up came a seven-headed dragon. His horse neighed, his falcon chattered, and his hound howled. The dragon struck his horse on the head.

'Neigh not, devil's carrion! chatter not, falcon! howl not, hound! for here is Little Rolling-pea. Now then,' said he, 'come forth, Little Rolling-pea! Shall we fight or try our strength?'

'Good youths travel not to try their strength, but only to fight.'

The combat began, and the heroes knocked off six of the dragon's heads. Only the seventh remained.

'Give me some breathing time!' the dragon said.

But Little Rolling-pea knocked off the last head also, cut out all the tongues, placed them in his knapsack, and threw the trunk into the river.

The comrades returned to the king, and brought the tongues for certain proof.

The third time they came at midnight to the bridge of rosewood. All at once, a nine-headed dragon came up. After the usual preliminaries, they began the combat, and the heroes beat off eight heads. Only the ninth remained.

Little Rolling-pea said: 'Give us some breathing time, unclean spirit!'

The dragon answered: 'Take breathing time or not, you will not overcome me. You slew my brothers by craft, not by strength.'

Little Rolling-pea not only fought, but pondered how to fool the dragon. 'Yes,' he said, 'there's still much of your brother behind you – I'll fight you both.'

'The dragon looked around quickly, and Little Rolling-pea cut off the ninth head also. He then cut out the tongues, put them into his knapsack, and threw the trunk into the river.

The king said, 'I thank you, mighty heroes! Live with God, and with joy and courage, and take as much gold and silver as you want.'

After this, the wives of the three dragons met together and took counsel. 'Where did those men come from who killed our husbands? Well, we shall be women indeed if we don't rid the world of them.'

The youngest said. 'Let us go to the highway where they will pass. I will turn myself into a beautiful wayside seat. When wearied, and they sit down upon it, it will be death to them all'.

The second said, 'If you fail, I will turn myself into an apple tree beside the highway. The agreeable fragrance will attract them. And when they taste the apples, it will be death to them all.'

Well, the heroes came up to the beautiful wayside seat. But Little Rolling-pea thrust his sword into it up to the hilt and blood poured forth!

They went on to the apple tree.

'Brother Rolling-pea,' said the heroes, 'let us eat an apple.'

But he said: 'If it is possible, let us eat; if it is not, let us go on further.'

He drew his sword and thrust it into the apple tree up to the hilt. Blood poured forth immediately.

So the third she-dragon chased after them, extending her jaws from the

earth to the sky.

Little Rolling-pea saw that there was no escape. He looked about and saw that she was coming directly towards him, so he threw the three horses into her mouth.

The she-dragon flew off to the sea to drink water, and the heroes proceeded further. She pursued them again. When Little Rolling-pea saw that she was near, he threw the three falcons into her mouth. Again the she-dragon flew to the sea to drink water, and they proceeded further.

But soon the she-dragon was again pursuing them. Seeing his danger, Little Rolling-pea threw the three hounds into her mouth. Again she flew off to the sea. While she drank her fill, they proceeded still further. After a while, Little Rolling-pea looked around and saw that she was catching up again. So he took his two comrades and threw them into her mouth.

The she-dragon flew to the sea to drink water, and he went on. But again she overtook him. He looked around, saw that she was not far off, and prayed, 'Lord, protect me and save my soul!'

He saw suddenly before him an iron workshop, and fled into it.

The smiths said to him: 'Why are you so fearful, stranger?'

'Honourable gentlemen!' he cried. 'Protect me from an unclean spirit, and save my soul!'

So the smiths shut themselves in the smithy.

'Give me what is mine!' cried the she-dragon from outside.

'Stick your tongue under the door,' the smiths said to her, 'and we will place Little Rolling-pea on it.'

So she thrust her tongue under the door. The three smiths seized it with their red-hot pincers, and said, 'Come, stranger, do what you will with her!'

Little Rolling-pea went outside and began to beat the she-dragon. He pounded her skin to the bones, and her bones to the marrow. Then he took her whole carcass and buried her seven fathoms deep. And then, and not till then, did he live and eat.

'Little Rolling-pea certainly wasn't a very loyal companion,' Sean objected.

66

'It's only a story,' Eppy smiled. 'And pretty much the same story one hears all over the world.'

'You mean the pattern of events, I assume,' I said.

'Down to particulars. There's a very ancient legend behind them all. I heard a similar account in Scotland, of all places.'

'Scotland!'

'Ah, there is a tale behind the tales, to be sure. It may be the most ancient of all, except the stories of Zu and Tiamat. It finds expression in the lore of India, China and Japan, Russia, Norway and Sweden, France and Italy, Holland, Scotland, and England. It's variously called *The Widow's Son*, *Shortshanks*, *Straparola*, *The Fisher's Son*, *The Smith's Son*, and by many other names.

'Frankly, it may well be Irish in origin, which wouldn't be at all surprising, since ours is the oldest of the European mythologies,' Eppy said not without a little pride. I hadn't realized that he counted himself as Irish. His notions were rarely provincial and I thought of him as ageless. 'But the early Celts may have brought it all the way from Scythia, for all I know. And probably did. But a good story is a good story, as the saying goes.'

'Does it?' Sean asked.

'It does now,' Eppy said. His voice had a little edge to it and Sean decided to keep his peace.

'It was part of a long story told by an old fisherman from Mull,' Eppy continued. 'Not surprisingly, it was called *The Fisher's Son*. It has about ten other names, of course, including *The Gray Lad* and *The Thirteenth Son of the King of Ireland* in which the hero, Sean Ruadh, disguises himself as a cowherd and rescues a king's daughter from a great sea-serpent which every seven years demands a princess to devour.

'In the Scottish version I heard, our hero is, of course, genuinely poor. There are the usual wonderful events in the beginning – his unusual birth, his remarkable growth to young manhood, and even the forging of three huge clubs for him by his old dad.

'This part of the saga begins when our hero sets out to make his way in the world.' Eppy paused because Sean had yawned mightily. Eppy gave one of his sniffs. 'Well, perhaps that tale about defeating a dragon can wait till another day.'

'I think it better had,' Sean said apologetically. Eyes on his wristwatch, he rose to his feet. 'For I have a ways to travel and the farm and all to attend to. You couldn't save the rest of this fascinating discussion until tomorrow, could you?'

'I don't see why not,' I said, and turned to Eppy. 'I'll feed you.'

'You will, will you? And let me sleep myself out in the morning, too?' Eppy cocked his head at me.

'Only if you promise to let me get a few words in edgeways.'

'Sure, an' it was yourself asked *me*,' he said, jamming his thumb into his chest.

'I'll just go quietly now,' Sean said and did so.

As soon as he had left, Eppy gave me a sideways look, jerking his thumb toward the door. 'You'd think he'd give us just a hint of why he's listening to all this, wouldn't you?'

'The biter bite?' I asked, grinning. 'No doubt he'll tell us in his own good time. Why should you care with a warm place to sleep and the promise of being fed for a few days?'

'He got *very* interested whenever hoards were mentioned, didn't he?' and Eppy rubbed his hands together.

'Yes, he did, but who'd expect a dragon hoard in Ireland!' I said. 'Anyway, I'm too tired to think. You know where your bed is. I've got to lock up.'

Dinner Break

SEAN EVANS PHONED me just after lunch and asked if Eppy was still here and could he be encouraged to talk more about dragons.

'None of those mentioned last night fit your bill?' I asked.

'Not really. I thought I'd learn from you what I needed to know in a short session.'

'Eppy does go on, doesn't he?' I said amiably.

Sean hesitated, then added: 'Is he all right?'

'D'you mean, discreet? Yes, indeed. I'd trust him more than anyone else I've met. Actually, you're very lucky Eppy just happened along.' I wasn't all that certain that Epiphanius Tighe had "just happened along" at all. 'He really does know the old dragons. And that seems to be the kind you need to know about?'

I heard a sigh.

'I don't know. I really don't know.'

'Well, come along. Eppy's still here. In fact, he's still in bed.'

'I'll be there as soon as I can.'

Which was quite long enough for Eppy to have a long bath, a big breakfast and read the *Irish Times* from cover to cover. He really got value out of that newspaper. I don't think he missed a single advertisement. And could undoubtedly quote them all back to me if I asked. I stocked up the fridge with all the beer I had on hand.

The Pajero swung down the drive and Sean emerged, looking a lot fresher than I felt.

'So you're back again, are you?' said Eppy.

'If you don't mind my sitting in on your sessions with Anne?' Sean said politely.

'No, not at all.' Eppy grinned, his knowing eyes twinkling. 'You haven't heard the half of what I know about dragons.'

If Sean's eyes glazed a bit, he recovered and settled down at the table again, nodding at Eppy to continue.

'I didn't mention the oriental dragons last night and they have a distinctly different cast of countenance and manner.

'One of my favourite old Chinese dragons, although a malevolent one, was called Ch'ih Yu. He had eight fingers, eight toes, and his head was covered with bristles.'

I couldn't suppress a giggle. 'I can see why you like him. Wayland Long is an imperial dragon and has five fingers so he can turn pages.'

'Why does a dragon need to turn pages?' Sean asked.

'Not now.' Eppy said to me firmly. 'Furthermore, your comparison of me and Ch'ih Yu is faulty, Anne,' he added, indignantly, wiggling both sets of five fingers dramatically. 'And I am not a bit malevolent. Please pay attention.

'Unlike western dragons, which are almost always rapacious, ravenous, horrible, and thoroughly wicked, if not the very devil himself, Chinese and Asian dragons tend to be destructive at worst and, at best, not only benevolent, but the source of many of nature's blessings.

'Early Chinese dragons were sometimes fierce and lecherous and required restraint. But, under Buddhist influence, they came to resemble the Nagas, the India serpent-dragon, especially in their beneficial aspect. *Tien-lung* were celestial dragons, who supported the mansions of the gods. Spiritual or divine dragons, *Shen-lung* could sometimes be seen ascending as clouds and descending as rain. *Ti-lung*, earth dragons, controlled rivers and springs. *Fu-ts'ang-lung* guarded underground treasures, gems and precious metals.

'Chinese dragons mate and lay eggs, nearly always near rivers. Have you one nearby, Sean?' Eppy asked.

'A river? Hmmm, yes, in fact, we do,' Sean said. I had noticed

that his fidgeting was on the increase but these had been long sessions.

'It only takes sixty days for Pernese dragons to produce. How long for the Chinese?' I asked.

'Oh, these incubate for a thousand years, or even three thousand, according to some authorities.'

'And I thought an elephant had a long gestation period.' I said with a groan of sympathy for pregnant dragons.

'They also hatch their young under water, amid thunder and lightning. So, here again is the draconic affinity with water.

'Now Ch'ih Yu was apparently a river–god, since he came out of the River Siang. He attacked the Yellow Emperor, who marshalled a war-band against him consisting of bears, panthers, tigers, and other land animals.

'Finally the emperor sent a winged dragon, Ying Lung, to fight Ch'ih Yu. Ying Lung gathered the waters against Ch'ih Yu, who retaliated with wind and rain, which flooded the earth.'

'A battle of storm–gods?'

'No doubt. So the Yellow Emperor sent his daughter to stop the rain. Afterwards, Ying Lung pursued and killed Ch'ih Yu. And that is one reason why the Chinese say when there is a fierce storm raging that the dragons are fighting.

'Japanese dragons, like their Chinese cousins, can be either kind or sinister. Sometimes they are even in need of a little support from a willing human.

'One of the more ancient accounts, sometimes called the *State Dragon Myth*, or the *Story of Susanowo Mikado*, tells of a malicious eight-headed dragon with eight tails who came every year and devoured one of the virgin daughters of an old couple who lived near the head of the river Hinokami at Idzumo. Moved to compassion by the old couple's plight, not to mention their having only one remaining daughter, the divine hero Susanowo and his son prepare eight tubs of sake and leave them where the dragon will find them.

'Unable to resist the aperitif, each head gulps down a barrel of the potent rice wine. And when the dragon falls unconscious, Susanowo and his son chop its heads off. He subsequently finds in one of the tails a marvelous sword the dragon had stolen from Amaterasu, the sun-goddess, who was Susanowo's sister.'

'Despite the rice wine, that sounds remarkably like Perseus and Andromeda,' I said.

'Dragons tend to follow the same customs the world over.' Eppy said solemnly. 'But the story of Tawara Toda, the famous warrior of the eleventh century, reveals a slightly different side of dragon family home life.

'One night, as Toda was crossing the outlet of Lake Biwa, he came upon a huge serpent sunning itself on the bridge. Being a famous Samurai, he passed by calmly, as if it were nothing out of the ordinary. Later that night a beautiful young woman came to his house. She explained that she admired him for the courage and tranquility he had shown earlier on the bridge, for, she admitted bashfully, the serpent was none other than the young lady herself. Moreover, she was the daughter of the great Dragon King who dwells under the lake.

'She then humbly begs Toda to accept a great challenge. A monstrous centipede has been killing many of her kinfolk. No one had been able to stop it.

'Being a very famous Samurai, Toda eagerly accepts the quest and returns to the bridge. Soon enough, he sees two brilliant lights coming across the lake – the glowing eyes of the giant centipede!

'Toda fires two arrows at those shining eyes. But the arrows are repelled by the monster's tough hide. Remembering that human spittle is fatal to centipedes, Toda spits on another arrow and shoots it at the centipede.

'With a horrible screech, the monster sinks down dead. And thus the dragon people are saved from extermination.

'On the following night, the dragon princess returns to thank Toda for his gallant assistance and invites him to accompany her to the palace of the Dragon King. They enter the waters of Lake Biwa, and once in the palace, the grateful dragons provide Toda with every delight that water can produce. As he is leaving, the Dragon King gives him three gifts. The first is a bale of rice which can never fail. The second is a roll of silk which provides an endless supply of cloth. And the third is a bell from India which had been hidden at the bottom of the lake for many centuries.

'Toda presents the bell to a temple, but keeps the other treasures for himself. And because of the unfailing rice-bale, he comes to be known as Tawara Toda, "Lord Toda of the Rice-bale." '

'Charming,' I said, then added. 'Could the gifts be considered part of a hoard?'

'Undoubtedly. Both Chinese and Japanese dragons love beautiful and valuable things. But the benign dragons are not terribly jealous, and under certain circumstances, are often very generous.'

'That might be more reassuring if we were in Japan,' Sean muttered. 'How about, er, Irish dragons?'

'Celtic dragons are pretty much like other dragons,' Eppy said. 'Welsh dragons are fierce and can be quarrelsome, as we have seen, but they tend toward drunkenness rather than lunching on the populace. On the other hand, the medieval Irish and Scottish variety preferred to dine on princess, but would settle for a knight or just about anything if hungry enough.'

'But there *were* Irish dragons?' I asked.

'Oh, yes. Some famous ones, as I said the other night. To be sure, Gottfried von Strassburg spiced up the story of Tristan quite a lot, and it could be argued that *his* dragon wasn't really Irish at all.'

'And the hoard?' Sean asked.

'Well, Irish dragons do sometimes have them. But the earliest is purely a princess-type, if you know what I mean.'

'I'm afraid I do.'

'There is a nice reversal, none the less, which we might have expected from the Old Irish. It's in a splendid account of a water-dragon from the Ulster Cycle. Of course, other heroes had a bit of trouble with wurrums – Conchobar MacNessa, Cuchulainn, and Finn MacCumhail, as well as saints such as Abban, Brendan, Columcille, Fechin, and Mochua, and Molua, and Colman of Dromore. But the story of Fraech, from the *Táin Bó Fráich*, is surely one of the oldest.'

'Fraech was one of the most handsome youths in all Ireland, and surely it

was no wonder, for it was well believed that his mother was one of the Sidhe, the Fairy Folk.

'Findabair, the daughter of Queen Maeve and Ailill of Connaught, fell deeply in love with him. So he came to Cruachan to win her. But, being greedy as well as loathe to lose their daughter, Maeve and Ailill set the bride-price so high that Fraech's honor is offended and he prepares to depart.

'Fearing that he and Findabair might elope and bring a host of the men of Ireland against them, Maeve and Ailill plot his death. In the guise of a hunting party, they catch up with Fraech's band. Thereafter they set off to the river to bathe.

' "Fraech," says Ailill, "I am told that you are expert in water. Get into this pool that we may behold your skill."

' "What kind of pool is it?" Fraech asks.

' "We know of no danger in it," ' Ailill says, "and bathing in it is frequent."

'So Fraech strips off his clothes and dives into the pool.

' "Do not come out of the water," says Ailill, "until you bring me a branch from the rowan tree that grows on the further shore, for Maeve values its beautiful berries."

'Now the rowan is a sacred tree, and its berries can kill. Moreover, it is believed that a spirit dwells in its roots. To harm a rowan tree is therefore unwise. Nonetheless, Fraech swims to the opposite shore, breaks a branch off the tree, and brings it on his back across the water. When Findabair sees him, she claims that she has never seen a youth who could come up a half or third to him for beauty.

'Fraech throws the branch out of the water to Ailill and Maeve. "Lovely and beautiful are the berries," they cry. "Bring us more of them."

'Off he goes again. But as he comes to the middle of the pool, the aroused water-serpent attacks.

' "Give me a sword," Fraech cries, "The monster has laid hold of me."

'None of the men on the shore will dare give one to him for fear of Ailill and Maeve. But fair Findabair strips and takes up his sword and leaps into the water. Enraged, Ailill casts a five-pronged spear at her. Fraech, however, catches the spear in his hand, and hurls it back, piercing Ailill's purple robe and tunic. All the while the dragon has him in its grip.

'But Findabair places the sword in Fraech's hand. Quickly, he cuts off the monster's head and brings the body to land. And from this the pool is named *Duiblind Fráich*, Fraech's Black Pool, in the lands of the men of Connaught.

'Afterwards, Ailill and Maeve return to their fortress. Fraech is brought there for healing, but how he is cured by the ministrations of his mother and the Sidhe, I cannot tell here, nor how he betroths the fair Findabair, nor how he meets his doom in the water at the hands of the great Cuchulainn. For those are other tales.'

'Nothing about a hoard, then?' asked Sean.

Eppy smiled mischievously. 'Not unless you consider a rowan tree sacred.'

I could almost hear the wheels turning in Sean's mind.

'Dragon hoards seem to interest you the most,' I said as diffidently as I could.

He flushed. Then he turned to Eppy and let out a now-I'll-tell-you-sigh. 'I have a problem which I think has to do with dragons, which is why Anne has been pumping you for me.'

Eppy grinned. He'd figured that one out last night but I didn't

mention it. 'May I ask for your discretion as well as your help?' Sean asked.

'Most certainly,' was Eppy's sincere reply, but I could see anticipatory tension in the old boy's posture.

Sean gave a shake to his upper body which was like a convulsion. He retrieved his waxed jacket and reached into one pocket. The unmistakable sound of jingling could be heard. Eppy's eyes brightened and I think he held his breath. I know I did, as Sean casually dribbled onto the table a collection of coins, some big uncut gemstones, and a very unusual, antique heavy gold chain. Eppy agitatedly rubbed his fingertips together and all but drooled as Sean hauled out more treasures from the other pocket, two more elaborate chains and a small blue-glass, hinged compact.

He gestured for us to examine them and Eppy all but fell off his chair when he reached for some of the jewels. Sean ran his fingers over the scattered coins, identifying each as he went.

'This is Phoenician, gold. This one Greek, Spartan in fact. These funny ones are Persian – same era. Roman, Egyptian and Carthaginian.'

'I didn't know there were any of them left,' Eppy said in a muted and awed whisper as he picked the Carthaginian one out of the pile.

'No elephant on it,' I remarked facetiously, which wasn't kind.

'The rouge-pot,' and Sean plunked the item in my hand, 'seems to have been made out of a single sapphire.'

I nearly dropped the thing I was so startled and then, turning it over in my hand, opened it up to disclose faint pinkish-red traces remaining in the gold lining. Any rabbit's foot that might have been used to apply it was long since gone.

'I've assayed the uncut gems,' Sean went on, a half smile on his face for the effect the items were having on both of us. 'They're genuine.' He forestalled my next question with a raised hand. 'I did all the testing and research myself.'

'Prudent of you,' Eppy said without looking up.

'I've a degree in chemistry, you see, before I got saddled with the family farm.'

'And you've been going over the family acres with a metal detector?' I asked.

He shrugged, spreading his hands in a self-deprecating gesture. 'Why not? The Derrynaflan Hoard was discovered with one, and *they'd* grown up with the same sort of family legend about hidden treasure that I did.'

'The Derrynaflan Hoard had nothing to do with dragons,' Eppy said with a little snort of disapproval, carefully returning the last of the coins to the table and reaching for one of the chains. 'That was merely a case of being too clever at restricting the knowledge of the site.'

'You have a family legend about treasures?' I asked Sean, fascinated by the idea.

'Yes, but only that there was one, a vast one,' and he grinned as he spread his fingers to encompass said "vast" treasure, 'but one that would also make the farm secure forever.' He gave an odd sort of shrug. 'I'd stopped believing in that one by the time

I was twelve. Only . . .' He smiled wryly.

'Only these came to light . . .' and Eppy grinned back at him, looking more like a treasure-guarding gnome than ever.

I caressed the beautifully faceted rouge-pot. It was something out of Prester John, or Aladdin's cave. 'And nothing more specific than that there *was* treasure?'

'My cousins and I used to think it might be gold that the Vikings had stolen and hidden. Ireland had rich gold-mines in Viking days.'

'Vikings melted gold down,' Eppy said contemptuously. 'What you have here is most emphatically not Viking loot. And, granted, Phoenician traders came to Ireland for tin, copper and gold, this . . .' and he threw up his hands, 'is actually far more likely . . .' he shook his head as if he didn't really like to say it aloud, 'to be part of dragon treasure.'

'The Blanpied dragons?' I asked Eppy, since that particular manifestation had been around a very long time; in fact, according to the Blanpied, these dragons were the ones involved in the Medieval epidemic of dragons. They were also inveterate hoarders, having started when the world began. When they didn't have enough to satisfy them, they had no scruples about "taking" over the hoard of another, less fortunate member of their species.

Eppy's eyes narrowed. 'Hmmm. But, no,' and he dismissed that with a wave of his hand.

'No, what ?' Sean demanded.

'No, that this is unlikely to be the Blanpied Manifestation because I've read nothing in the papers about massive livestock slaughtering,' Eppy said. 'Not around here at any rate.' He peered sharply across at Sean Evans. 'Any killings where you live?'

'Not even dog packs worrying my sheep,' Sean said shaking his head emphatically. 'Why?'

'Well, that's the way you identify Blanpied Dragon Manifestations. Their last known appearance was in the Middle Ages.'

'You didn't mention those with the others you've told me about,' Sean said, almost accusingly.

'Well, the Blanpied Dissertation about dragons is somewhat suspect and not documented enough to suit me,' Eppy said with a sniff of disapproval.

'I only mention the Dissertation because the dragons discussed were such great hoarders.' I explained. 'Look, couldn't this be plain treasure trove?' I threw the question out at Eppy but he was concentrating on the links of the heavy chain in his hand. Now *where* had the jeweller's loupe he was using come from? Ah, well, Eppy's old baggy trousers could hide a lot more than his skinny self. 'There were a lot of Irish pirates, always raiding the Britons, even in Arthur's days. And later on, the English press-ganged lots of Irish sailors. If it *is* treasure trove, you'll need your T.D.* on your side.'

'My T.D. would likely be a lot easier to deal with than a dragon,' Sean said grimly.

'Quite likely,' I replied, but I could see that Sean, at least, was convinced that he had found a dragon hoard. Looking over at Eppy's expression, the old codger did, too: more certainly than Sean did.

'I heard from you,' Sean went on, 'that dragons always know when their hoard is in danger. That's why I need to know how to deal with a dragon. I happen to *need* the money these could fetch – to save the family farm.' His brief grin had no humour in it.

'Then I'd sell the stuff real quick and let the new owner worry about the dragon,' I said.

Sean gave me a long and searching look. 'I don't think I want to do that, dragon or not.'

'Smart of you,' Eppy said, gathering the coins into one pile and the uncut gems into another. 'Because it's my considered opinion that you have indubitably discovered a dragon's hoard.'

'So what do I do about it?'

Eppy stretched. 'It's very late . . .'

Well, I was glad that someone had noticed that. Even with the surge of energy all that treasure had given me, I was fast fading on my feet.

'Yes, it is,' Sean said, scooping up everything while Eppy wistfully watched him pocket it all again. 'I'll bring some other pieces that I haven't been able to date tomorrow. But I do manage a farm and I'll have to be up early in the morning, as usual, and tend it.'

'Then come back tomorrow for dinner and maybe we can figure out just what sort of a dragon you've got on your farm,' I said. 'Six-thirty?'

'You'll be here?' Sean asked Eppy.

I snorted, glancing at the old man who wouldn't turn down a free meal.

'I 'spect so,' he said amiably without glancing in my direction.

By the time I had seen Sean out and locked the doors, Eppy had already left the kitchen so I took myself, and Saffron, to my room and gratefully crawled into my own bed.

* A Speaker of The House (Gaelic).

Over Dinner

I MADE ONE of my favourite tuna fish casseroles because Eppy does eat fish, and lots of vegetables, including the obligatory two types of potatoes, and I baked a pie.

Promptly at six-thirty, the Pajero turned into the driveway. Sean emerged, carefully placed some odd-shaped parcels on a case of lager, and entered the house.

'My turn to supply the beer,' he said, putting his burden down briefly on the counter. Then, with a flourish, he handed me a florist's cellophane sheaf; mixed stargazers and carnations.

'That's very thoughtful of you, Sean,' I said, very pleased at such thoughtfulness.

'I'll just put the beer in the fridge?'

'Please.'

'I thought you weren't here,' he added, stowing beer deftly, 'when I didn't see your car in the drive.'

I chuckled. 'For my sins, I've let Eppy borrow it for some books he needs from his place. You're really going to get chapter and verse on dragons tonight. A real identity parade.'

He gasped, pointing, and I swivelled to see my Camry just missing the left hand gate-post as Eppy careened back into my yard. If I hadn't seen the performance before, and known my car would live through it, I would have blanched as he did.

'He has this relationship with mechanical things . . .'

'You're kidding . . .'

'As you've just witnessed,' I said, because the car had come to a gravel-spraying stop just short of the front door.

Then we both saw Eppy piling tome after tome into one arm, and stuffing a few scrolls under the other. He made his zig-zag way to the front door which Sean made haste to open.

'Ah!' Eppy said, sniffing at the aroma as he passed the oven. With some care he arranged what he had brought at the opposite end of the table to where I had set our places for dinner. 'Can we eat now?'

'Of course,' I said equably and, when Sean indicated by look and gesture that he was willing to help, I jerked my head toward the fridge.

'Ah, yes, the beer!'

By mutual accord, nothing was said about dragons during dinner. Eppy was generally single-minded when it came to food and Sean ate as neatly and with good relish.

Eppy required two pieces of the apple pie to sate himself and I knew he had mentally marked a third slice for later in the evening. We all cleared the table and settled to coffee . . . and dragons.

'I checked with my neighbours and the local rag,' Sean said, starting off. 'There've been no unexplained animal deaths at all. Anywhere in Ireland.'

'Well, that's the Blanpieds out of the running,' I said, relieved, for they were a rather nasty lot.

Eppy pursed his lips, looking very thoughtful.

'I also think I'm running out of time,' Sean added.

'Really?' Eppy's eyes went wide and his eyebrows reached his non-existent hairline. 'Why?'

Sean reached into his pocket and spilled a load of bright, shiny, obviously brand-new coins onto the table: silver Irish punts; multi-faceted English gold-coloured pounds, and some oddments from other countries.

'I found these when I put back what I'd shown you last night. Their appearance makes me nervous.'

'It would appear that the owner of your hoard is alive, well, and collecting on a regular basis,' Eppy said with considerable sang-froid, but I noticed an eagerness in his manner, which had heretofore been "laid-back."

'Some of the old orms hoarded treasure, some preferred to devour maidens and youths, some did it all,' he said in a far too casual manner. 'None had a very good reputation, and, in truth, they all suffered from a bad press.'

'That's why I wrote about Pern dragons,' I said, 'to establish a better press image for the whole kaboodle.'

'You certainly did that, m'dear,' Eppy said.

'Wait a minute. Go back. Orms?' Sean asked.

'Worm, Orm, Wurrum – dragons go by many names. *Drake* is a common nick-name. As a taxonomist, I take careful note of variations,' Eppy said. 'Many are just regional or dialectical differences. But there is a great difference between, say, a gryphon, or griffon, which is an eagle-headed winged lion often having four legs, and a wyvern, which is always a two-legged, winged dragon with a serpent's tail. A *nicker*, on the other hand, is your garden-variety water-monster. It comes from an old German word for crocodile. But it also resembles the Greek word *nix*, from which we get *nixie*, or water-nymph, what the old Irish called a *nigid*.'

'I see,' I said, but clearly didn't, because Eppy gave me a trenchant look.

'Certain extinct saurians,' he said, 'including flying models such as the *pteranodon* and *pterydactyl*, have been proposed as primitive dragons. Conversely, dragons have been proposed to be the last vestiges of such primeval *pterosaurs*. As with theories of ancient astronauts, such proposals are regarded by professional dracologists as heroic but pathetic. Attempts to explain dragons away while acknowledging their reality.'

'What if,' I began, 'dragons, like angels and Flying Saucers, became what they were thought to be like? That is, actually came to resemble the images we have of them according to the dominant cultural assumptions, et cetera?'

'Hmmm,' Eppy said, and I could see that I had startled him with that theory. 'In the ancient science of alchemy, which is as old as China and as current as that odd fellow who lives down the glen from me, the dragon was always used as a symbol. Sometimes it stood for the Great Work itself.'

'The, er, Great Work?' Sean asked.

'Alchemy, the Great Work, Transmutations. Indeed, whether transmuting baser metals into gold, or, much more importantly, transforming the alchemist himself – or herself, I hasten to add – into a higher form. Sometimes two dragons, male and female, are portrayed devouring each other as a preparation for entering the glorified state of total unity. The dragon could also stand for the primal form of matter which contained the seed of gold.

'More commonly, the dragon was a symbol for the element mercury, largely because of its double nature, being both a fluid and a metal, that is, solid and liquid. Mercury was therefore called the Seed of the Dragon, and some philosophers called the dragon Hermes' Bird. Hermes is the same as Mercury, of course.'

'All very reasonable, I'm sure,' I murmured politely.

'There are pictures in the old manuals showing a man cutting open a dragon to obtain a precious jewel from its heart or brain . . .'

'Aerin did that in *The Hero and the Crown*, the last drop of blood from Maur's heart,' I said.

Eppy gave me a stern stare. '. . . which may have something to do with obtaining the legendary Philosopher's Stone from cooking a mixture of sulphur, mercury, and a salt. When the dragon is pictured as nailed to a cross, that symbolizes the fixation of the volatile during various alchemical processes.

'Very symbolical, those old chemists. But, you know, I have it on fairly good authority that a few of them did make gold. Like those Rawn dragons of yours.' Then Eppy gave another of his long "hmmmms".

'Hoards?' Sean asked remindingly.

'Smaug was the first of the modern dragons known to hoard,' I said, 'both the last of the ancient dragons and the first of the

modern ones'.

'Dragons are also the repositories of ancient knowledge,' Eppy added, not to be elbowed out of any discussion about J. R. R. Tolkien. 'That is, if you are lucky enough to escape alive once you have the answers.'

'Which you'd love to do, wouldn't you?' I said, grinning at Eppy. 'Professor Tolkien actually had three types of drakes – the Smaug-type who can both fly and breathe fire, a second who snorts flame but can't fly and a cold-worm, no fly, no fire.'

'Smaug, past tense of the Germanic *Smaugen* – "to squeeze through a hole",' Eppy said. 'And it's also the old Norse equivalent of an old English charm, *wi smoegan wyrme* – "against the penetrating worm."'

'Do you mind?' I could see that Sean was totally confused by the erudition.

'Is there a possibility of this Smaug being on my farm? Now?' Sean asked. 'What was he like? I never read Tolkien.' He pretended to cower from our indignant reaction. 'Well, I wasn't much of a reader even as a lad. What *do* dragons look like? I mean, the kind you know, although the rest has been very interesting.'

'I've already told you what ancient dragons looked like,' Eppy said, piqued but gestured for me to answer.

'Generally speaking,' and I was glad to have a chance to with the way Epiphanius Tighe tended to dominate our evenings, 'dragons are big. The large bachelor/spinster uneconomical size, considering they generally eat a lot.'

'What *do* they eat?' Sean asked.

'Wedding dresses, with princesses in them for afters,' I said, 'and they show a marked taste for knight, mutton and treasure hunters. They also don't biodegenerate the way we humans do, so they can be ageless. I mean, Tiamat and some of Eppy's other golden oldies may still be alive.'

Sean shifted nervously about in his chair.

'We only have to figure out which one it is likely to be,' Eppy said as he rubbed his hands together in anticipation.

I went on. 'There're scaled dragons, mantled, spiney, taloned, bad-tempered, with talons for seizing things to chew with their long fangs. Some have nose-holes, or nostrils, like jet intakes. They display ears, headknobs, dorsal ridges, wings. The wings vary, too, though most dragons soar on thermals like raptors. All that mass to move through the air. Some draconic faces are even kindly. Dragon eyes can be irised, or have nictating lids like lizards or facets that change colour with their emotions to gold and silver, or huge eyes that are limitlessly, shiveringly black.' Sean recoiled as I made the most of such an awesome feature before I continued in a milder tone. 'In colour they range from white-hided ones to black. My Pernese dragons come in five different colours, plus one white sport. Generally black dragons are very old. And old ones get very big, too. Like Father Dragon in *The Elvenbane*. Or the ones in *Perilous Seas* who grow to such enormous size that their corpses make the start of hills. Griaule was so big that, when the wizard paralysed him, a village was established on one flank and its residents dug the earth to find his valuable scales.'

'There aren't any *small* ones?' asked Sean plaintively. 'For getting into national treasuries to steal their latest minting?'

'Lots,' I said blithely to reassure him. 'Silbakor could compress small enough to fit into a paperweight when he wasn't on duty and Pip is a mini-drag who sits on his friend's shoulder.'

'Your fire-lizards sit on shoulders, too,' Eppy put in.

'So they do, but they're not really dragons: they only resemble them,' I said.

'What sort do I have to contend with then?' Sean asked.

'We know you are dealing with a hoarder,' I said, ticking off that habit on my fingers . . .

'Possibly a shape-changer since you've never seen him,' Eppy said.

'Old, because of the objects in the hoard you've got,' I went on.

'Not necessarily old,' Eppy countered. 'It could have *acquired* that hoard . . . how big is the hoard, by the bye? Purely an academic question, you understand,' he added hastily.

'It fills a large space' Sean said after a pause in which he regarded each of us in turn. 'A very large space.'

'Underground?' Eppy asked. 'For identification purposes . . . and since no one in your family before you has found it.'

'I never said where,' Sean replied. 'Someone else did because the family were known to be pretty warm in the pocket through the seventeenth and eighteenth centuries.'

'Ah!' and Eppy smiled. 'Some member of your family did not happen to go to China in those centuries, did he?'

'You mean, China trade?' Sean asked.

'I didn't think we *had* trade with China in the sixteen and seventeen hundreds,' I said at the same time.

'I don't think so,' Sean said, answering Eppy. Then he grinned. 'We always had some member of the family "travelling".'

'For his health?' I asked, cocking an eyebrow at Sean.

'Yes, the wild one of the family sent off to keep down the scandal,' Sean said. 'Could well have made it to the Far East, I suppose.'

'Irish engineers built the fortifications in ol' San Juan, Puerto Rico,' I said. 'Wild goosing. Why did you ask?' I turned to Eppy with that question.

'Hmmm. It's just a possibility. Remember, there is a Chinese dragon who by tradition guards *underground* treasures, gems and precious metals,' he said, picking at his lower lip. 'The entry was sealed?'

Sean nodded.

'Ah,' came from Eppy again and he rubbed his hands once more, 'so your dragon would have to be a shape-changer to get into the place. They are more apt to insinuate themselves where others couldn't.'

'Where no others have gone before,' I said, grinning at the parody.

'Is that good?' Sean asked.

'Well, a lot of shape-changers were good,' I said. 'In fact, quite maternal. One in particular . . .'

Eppy groaned as I reached for the thick book of *The Elvenbane*.

Nothing veiled the brilliance of the sky, a clear and flawless turquoise bowl inverted over the undulating dunes of the desert, and the sun blazed in the east in solitary glory. Alamarana closed her inner eyelids against the white glare of sun-on-sand below, spread her wings until her muscles strained, and spiraled in an ever-lower circle in the thermal she had chosen. Her destination, the ruin of a long-abandoned dragon-lair complex, was hardly more than a flaw in the silver-gilt sand beneath her scarlet-and-gold wings, but the pool beside it was visible at any height, reflecting the sky above like an unwinking cerulean eye.

She corrected her course with tiny changes in the web of her wings as she drifted a little away from her goal. Months ago she would have folded her wings tight to her body and plummeted down on the ruins from above, ending her dive in a glorious, sand-scattering backwash of braking wing-beats. Not today. Not while she still carried the little one; no recklessness when she would be risking two, not one, with her aerobatics.

She tilted her wings, spilled air, dropped a little, spilled air again. The spring-fed pool beckoned with a promise of serenity: she was tired, wing and shoulder muscles aching with the strain of so much flying, and glad this stop marked the end of her journey. Already she had spent her appointed time on Father Dragon's mountaintop, in the surf beneath the cliffs that stood sentry on the Northern Sea, and deep within the redolent tree-trunk "halls" of the endless cedars of Taheavala Forest. Thus she had joined with air, water, and earth – and this final station on her pilgrimage represented a melding with the element of fire. Not for all dragons, this pilgrimage of the elements, but for a shaman it was the nearest thing to mandatory the dragons ever came.

The heat felt wonderful after the chill of the upper air. For a moment she kept her wings spread, and soaked up the blessed sun-ray with her eyes half-closed and all four of her taloned claws digging happily into the burning sands. She wriggled her toes in luxury, revelling in the heat, and in the strength the sun's rays gave back to her. Within her, the little one stirred restlessly, bumping against her ribs. Her time would be soon, now, though unless she suffered some kind of strain, not until Alara willed it. That was one control, at least, that a female shaman had over her own biological destiny.

I am wasting time. The sooner I finish, the sooner I can be home. She turned her head slowly, looking for a good place to settle for her final meditation.

The ruin had been so long abandoned that there was little left of it. Its most notable feature was a single long, low wall, rising from drifts of shining sand like the spine of a snake, the sinuous curves typical of draconic workmanship. Beyond it, something square rose barely above the surface, the hints of a foundation, architecture copies from elves or humans. A heap of pink shapes marked the toppled sand-worn stones of what had been a tower. A few plants and scrawny grasses, a half dozen trees, were the only growing things: all were within half a dragon-length of the pool.

Beside the wall was the stone-rimmed pool itself, of course. Spring-fed, and colder than her kind preferred, it was so pure as to be dangerous to drink in any quantity, at least for dragons, who thrived on the alkaline salt-pools that poisoned other creatures.

This was not a site of disaster, nor even of ill-chance. There was no hint of violence here, only the work of time and the hand of nature.

Irilianale's Lair, it had been called. "As impulsive as Iri" was the saying and "More persuasive than Irilianale," by which the entire story could be implied. Iri had taken a liking to the spot, a desert oasis perfect for the heat-basking the dragons, with their high metabolism, craved . . .

The sand was soft and yielding, and silken against the scales of her sides. She contemplated the pool for a moment, letting its deep silent water give her the pattern for her meditations. Gradually she let her mind sink into it, down through the blue-tinged waters, into the indigo depths, to the sand-strewn bottom, where the cold water welled up from a hidden crack in the sands. There was the magic, welling up as serenely as the water, from the joining of the six shining ley-lines. She saw them with her overeyes, glowing moon-on-dragon-scale-silver, that peculiar sheen of pure metal with the overlay of draconic iridescence: a furtive rainbow that was all colours and none at all. And where the lines met, a silent fountain of power sang upward, rising toward the sunbeams lancing down to meet it.

She drew yet more of the power away from the spring, spinning it into a gossamer thread that sparkled to her innersight and caressed her with a rich and heady taste like the sparkling vintages she had enjoyed in her elven form. She took the power to herself and spun it through her body until she shimmered like a mirage from nose to tail-tip. Tension built in her, as she drank in more and more of the power, drank it in and held it until she could hold no more, until she strained with it as a water-skin filled nigh to bursting.

Now – she thought, and felt the ripple of change start at her tail and course through her in a wave, leaping in its wake –

Stone.

Not just any stone. Fire-born stone, the frozen wrath of volcanoes, the glassy blood from the heart of the world. The closest any living thing could come to fire itself.

In the blink of an eye, she shifted. *No* longer was there a dragon curled shining in the sun. In her place, the hollow of sand cupped a dull obsidian boulder, vaguely draconic in shape, smooth and sandworn as the stones of the wall behind her, taking in the blistering heat of the sun's rays and absorbing them into its dusty black surface.

Now she could relax and let her mind drift where it would. Four times she had shifted: into an ice-eagle, a species nearly as large as the dragons themselves and so at home with the currents of the upper airs that they ate and slept on the wing: into a careless delphin, as at one with the waters as the ice-eagle was in the air; into a mighty cedar, with roots deep in the soil – and now, most difficult of all because it was not living, the fire-stone. Not all female dragons need take their pilgrimage of powers when a birth was imminent; only the shamans, like Alara, to fix a oneness with this world into their offspring, in hopes that one or more would in turn take up shamanistic duties to serve dragonkind.[9]

'Maybe that's why you've had a dragon restant all these years,' Eppy said, grinning. 'It's a female and requires a safe haven for her offspring.'

'I hadn't considered that possibility,' Sean said, not at all reassured about it.

'Maybe that's why you've suddenly been able to find the hoard,' I suggested. 'She's about to produce again and left the door open so to speak.'

'No, I don't think so. I was repairing some drains in the . . .' Sean stopped.

'Oh, don't worry about us,' Eppy said. 'She's honest and I'm far more interested in the dragon than I am in the hoard, though, I admit, those were very tempting samples you showed us last night. And today.'

I could almost hear Eppy's unspoken question: *And couldn't you now trust us enough to show us the hoard site?*

'Why are *you* interested in the dragon?' Sean asked.

Eppy sighed, glanced over at me as if for my support, 'I'm a dragon hunter. Registered and approved.'

I should have asked then who had registered and approved him but Sean jumped in.

'Why do you hunt dragons? If not for the hoard?'

'Not all dragons have hoards as I have punctiliously informed you. And you can certainly go rooting out the great worms without their demise in mind. Ged sails halfway across EarthSea to put a few pertinent questions to a dragon. But then,' and he winked at Sean, 'he was rather better equipped to deal with them than you seem to be. Do you have Ursula Le Guin to hand, Anne, to elaborate for Sean?'

'Which had you in mind? His fight with the Dragon of Pendor or the confrontation with Orm Umbar?'

Eppy gave a flourish with his hand. 'Which ever you prefer, milady.'

'Well, the confrontation with Yevaud is quite dramatic, since it's only by knowing the name of the Dragon of Pendor that Ged is able to blackmail him into ceasing to raid the Ninety Isles.

I was now rifling through the pages of the *The Farthest Shore*, 'The confrontation with Orm Umbar is sensational: Ged, now the Archmage Sparrowhawk, has travelled with young Arren, the Prince of Enlad, to the very edge of the world in pursuit of the unknown and the terrible power that is unmaking the world, both of humans and dragonkind. Ah, here we are.'

He turned to go to the shelter, and Arren followed him. But the strangeness of that daybreak was not yet done, for even then, as the eastern rim of the sea grew white, there came from the north flying a great bird: so high up that its wings caught the sunlight that had not shone upon the world yet, and beat in strokes of gold upon the air. Arren cried out, pointing. The mage looked up startled. Then his face became fierce and exulting, and he shouted out aloud, 'Niam hietha arw Ged arivaissa! – which in the Speech of the Making is: If thou seekest Ged here find him.

And like a golden plummet dropped, with wings held high outstretched, vast and thundering on the air, with talons which might seize an ox as if it were a mouse, with a curl of steamy flame streaming from long nostrils, the dragon, stooped like a falcon on the rocking raft.

The raft-folk cried out: some cowered down, some lept into the sea, and some stood still, watching, in a wonder that surpassed fear.

The Dragon hovered above them. Ninety feet, maybe, was he from tip to tip of his vast membranous wings, that shone in the new sunlight like gold-shot smoke, and the length of his body was no less, but lean, arched like a greyhound, clawed like a lizard, and snake scaled. Along the narrow spine went a row of jagged darts, like rose thorns in shape, but at the hump of the back three feet in height, and so diminishing that the last of the tail-tip was no longer than the blade of a little knife. These thorns were gray, and the scales of the dragon were iron-gray, but there was a glitter in them. His eyes were green and slitted.

Moved by fear for his people to forget fear for himself, the chief of the raft-folk came from his shelter with a harpoon such as they used in the hunt of whales: it was longer than himself, and pointed with a great barbed point if ivory. Poising it on his small sinewy arm he ran forward to gain the impetus to hurl it up and strike the dragon's narrow, light-mailed belly that hung above the raft. Arren waking from a stupor saw him, and plunging forward caught his arm and came down in a heap with him and the harpoon. 'Would you anger him with your silly pins?' he gasped. 'Let the Dragonlord speak first!'

The chief, half the wind knocked out of him, stared stupidly at Arren, and at the mage, and at the dragon. But he did not say anything. And then the dragon spoke.

None there but Ged to whom it spoke could understand it, for dragons speak only in the Old Speech, which is their tongue. The voice was soft and hissing, almost like a cat's when he cries out softly in rage, but huge, and there was a terrible music in it. Whoever heard that voice stopped still, and listened.

The mage answered briefly, and again the dragon spoke, poising above him on slight-shifting wings: even, thought Arren like a dragonfly poised on the air.

Then the mage answered one word 'Momeas' I will come, and he lifted up his staff of yew-wood. The dragon's jaws dropped, and a coil of smoke escaped them in a long arabesque. The gold wings clapped like thunder, making a great wind that smelled of burning: and he wheeled and flew hugely to the north.

It was quiet on the rafts, with a little thin piping and wailing of children, and women comforting them; and men climbed aboard out of the sea somewhat shamefaced, and the forgotten torches burned in the first rays of the sun.

[. . .]

'That was Orm Embar,' (Sparrowhawk) said, 'the Dragon of Selidor, kin to the great Orm who slew Erreth-Akbe and was slain by him.'

'Was he hunting, lord?' said Arren; for he was not certain whether the mage had spoken to the dragon in welcome or in threat.

'Hunting me. What dragons hunt, they find. He came to ask my help'.[10]

Eppy sighed. 'Ged was a lot luckier than I. I wish a dragon would come hunting **me**.' He sighed again. 'I've always had to do the hunting. As far back as I can remember – and that is a long, *long* time . . . I'm fascinated by them.

'I saw my first one in Wales, actually,' and his voice turned melancholic, his gaze unfocused, calling up that memory. 'I was just a boy, so you can imagine how long ago *that* was! I was walking in the lovely green hills of Gwynedd, near Capel Curig. It was a warm summer's day and I decided to take a little snooze in the forest. Couldn't really help myself.

'I woke up an hour later. The sun had gone behind one of the high hills in the west, and the forest was delightfully cool and beginning to darken. A gentle breeze had sprung up and was rustling through the tops of the oak and pines.

'I stood up and stretched. It was then I saw it.'

'A dragon? A real one?' Sean asked in an eager, excited voice.

'Through the trees, I clearly perceived a great, long, sinuous form flowing in reptilian waves across the bottom of a small meadow not two hundred yards away. I rubbed my eyes and looked again. My heart skipped several beats, I can tell you, because it was still there.

'I was so excited, I forgot any thought of danger and approached quietly through the bushes and trees for a better view. But, when I came to the edge of the meadow, there was only a line of low bushes, swaying in the breeze.'

'So it wasn't a dragon after all.' The disappointment in Sean's voice was evident. Or was it relief?

'Ah,' and Eppy held one stubby finger up, his eyebrows reaching into his non-existent hairline, 'but it *was* a dragon! That's what I'm trying to explain.

'Dragons, you see, are not primarily physical entities, but spiritual energies. Forms of consciousness, if you will. They can materialize in different ways at different times to people in different parts of the world and in many different circumstances. Which is to say, that they look like what people *think* they ought to look like.' He gave me a wise glance.

'I don't understand,' Sean said.

'To become visible, the dragon power, or powers, have to take on the characteristics that make them perceptible as dragons at the time and place.'

Gwynedd, Na Wales, near Capel Curig 1925 first dragon!?

'What you needed was a Dragon Helm,' I said, for such a device, if there was one for starters, allowed the wearer to pierce the dragon's cloak of invisibility.

Eppy shot me a startled look which quickly turned into a scowl and he continued as if I hadn't spoken.

'. . . Like angels and Flying Saucers. Old Jung understood that. At least, after we had discussed it for a few hours.'

'Jung? *The* Jung?' I asked. Not that I was surprised that Eppy had met the man. He was old enough to have been young enough to meet such an eminent teacher.

'Carl Gustav himself,' and Eppy nodded. 'Splendid fellow. Lived in Zurich at the time. Nice city. Now *there* was a man who appreciated a good dragon story.'

'For his own purposes, no doubt!' I grinned.

'You see, Sean, essentially dragons are invisible,' Eppy said. 'We *make* them visible when we dream them, paint them, tell stories about them. I'm sure there are many people in the world who firmly believe that Anne's Pern dragons exist.' I nodded vigorously as Eppy went on. 'Other people can make them appear by magic or other means. Thus Smaug became real when Tolkien wrote his story, and his reality is confirmed whenever anyone reads *The Hobbit* and suspends the modern tendency to disbelief. Even for a little while.'

'Is that really where dragons come from?' Sean asked. 'But I don't believe in dragons. I never thought about dragons. And certainly if I hadn't discovered that hoard and heard – I don't know where now,' and he flapped his hand, dismissively, 'that dragon hoard, I wouldn't have bothered Anne here. But a dragon hoard is the only logical explanation for what I found.'

'You've shown us proof of that,' and Eppy pointed towards Sean's jacket.

'If it's not for the hoard, then why do you hunt dragons, Eppy?' Sean asked.

'Well,' and Eppy grinned 'I'm no Ged. Actually, I'm a psycho-taxonomist, Sean. My job is to catalogue all the various manifestations of dragon powers so we can understand them better. And ourselves as well.'

'Ourselves?'

'And everything else. You see, the story of the dragon, the hero, and the princess is the most fundamental myth of all. It covers everything from the origin of the cosmos to the deeply unconscious aspects of the human mind. There *is* a little dragon in all of us, you know.'

'I'd agree to that,' I said equably. 'How many have you catalogued?'

'Fourteen thousand, seven hundred and twenty-nine.'

'Fourteen *thousand*?' I exclaimed, thinking of the pauky hundred and fifty I had discovered in the realms of science fiction and fantasy.

'. . . seven hundred and twenty-nine. Yours, Sean, will make fourteen thousand seven hundred and thirty. Manifestations, that is. There are types of families of dragons, of course, which share a number of characteristics . . .'

'As we've been telling you,' I put in.

'Originally, of course, dragons didn't fly. They didn't have wings. Those came later. Like multiple heads, scales, claws and fiery breath. And colours.'

'Do you mean . . . they evolved?'

'Something like that. Chinese dragons grow long whiskers, but Welsh and Mayan dragons don't. Some dragons have four legs, others two, and some even six. The majority have taken to breathing fire, however. And flying. And, of course, collecting things. Most of the polycephalic manifestations disappeared a couple of hundred years ago. Fortunately so, given that they were also largely fire-breathing.'

'And mine? My manifestation?' Sean asked urgently. 'What's mine?'

Eppy spread both hands. 'I don't know enough about him or her yet. Tell me this, Sean,' and Eppy leaned forward. 'When you visit the hoard – wherever it is, do you sense any aura?'

'Aura?'

'Malevolence can be palpable,' I suggested. 'And it's more apt to be sensed than benignity. But there are good dragons. There are dragons that *have* to have people. Or rather, a special personality that attracts the dragon. And I don't need to read this one,' I said in an aside to Eppy.

Lessa turned resolutely back to the rocking golden egg, knowing what to expect, and trying to divine what the successful boys had, or had not done, that caused the baby dragons to single them out.

A crack appeared in the golden shell and was greeted by the terrified screams of the girls. Some had fallen into little heaps of white fabric, others embraced tightly in their mutual fear. The crack widened and the wedge-head broke through, followed quickly by the neck, gleaming gold. Lessa wondered with unexpected detachment how long it would take the beast to mature, considering its by no means small size at birth. For the head was larger than that of the male dragons and they had been large enough to overwhelm sturdy boys of ten full Turns.

Lessa was aware of a loud hum within the Hall. Glancing up at the audience, she realized it emanated from the watching bronze dragons, for this was the birth of their mate, their queen. The hum increased in volume as the shell shattered into fragments and the golden glistening body of the new female emerged. It staggered out, dipping its sharp beak into the soft sand, momentarily trapped. Flapping its wet wings, it righted itself, ludicrous in its weak awkwardness. With sudden and unexpected swiftness, it dashed toward the terror-stricken girls.

Before Lessa could blink, it shook the first girl with such violence, her head snapped audibly and she fell limply to the sand. Disregarding her, the dragon leaped towards the second girl but misjudged the distance and fell, grabbing out with one claw for support and raking the girl's body from shoulder to thigh. The screaming of the mortally injured girl distracted the dragon and released the others from their horrified trance. They scattered in panicky confusion, racing, running, tripping, stumbling, falling across the sand toward the exit the boys had used.

As the golden beast, crying piteously, lurched down from the raised arena toward the scattered women, Lessa moved. Why hadn't that silly clunk-headed girl stepped aside, Lessa thought, grabbing for the wedge-head, at birth not much larger than her own torso. The dragon's so clumsy and weak, she's her own worst enemy.

Lessa swung the head round so that the many-faceted eyes were focused to look at her . . . and found herself lost in that rainbow regard.

A feeling of joy suffused Lessa, a feeling of warmth, tenderness, unalloyed affection and instant respect and admiration flooding mind and heart and soul. Never again would Lessa lack an advocate, a defender, an intimate, aware instantly of the temper of her mind and her heart, of her desires. How wonderful was Lessa, the thought intruded into Lessa's reflections, how pretty, how kind, how thoughtful, how brave and clever!

Mechanically, Lessa reached out to scratch the exact spot on the soft eye ridge.

The dragon blinked at her wistfully, extremely sad that she had distressed Lessa. Lessa reassuringly patted the slightly damp, soft neck that curved trustingly toward her. The dragon reeled to one side and one wing fouled on the hind claw. It hurt. Carefully, Lessa lifted the erring foot, freed the wing, folding it back across the dorsal ridge with a pat.

The dragon began to croon in her throat, her eyes following Lessa's every move. She nudged as Lessa obediently attended the other eye ridge.

The dragon let it be known she was hungry.

'We'll get you something to eat directly,' Lessa assured her briskly and blinked back at the dragon in amazement. How could she be so callous? It was a fact that this little menace had just now seriously injured, if not killed, two women.

She wouldn't have believed her sympathies could swing so alarmingly toward the beast. Yet it was the most natural thing in the world for her to wish to protect this fledgling.

The dragon arched her neck to look Lessa squarely in the eye. Ramoth repeated wistfully how exceedingly hungry she was, confined so long in that shell without nourishment.

Lessa wondered how she knew the golden's dragon name and Ramoth replied: Why shouldn't she know her own name since it was hers and no one else's? And then Lessa was lost again in the wonder of those expressive eyes.

Oblivious to the descending bronze dragons, uncaring of the presence of their riders, Lessa stood caressing the head of the most wonderful creature on all Pern, fully prescient of troubles and glories, but most immediately aware that Lessa of Pern was Weyrwoman to Ramoth, the Golden, now and forever.[11]

'Well, certainly nothing like that occurs when I'm in the hoard . . .

place . . .' Sean said, almost wistfully. 'Your kind of dragon would make an amazing friend. Are there ones like that in the real world? I mean, nowadays,' he asked Eppy.

'If there were, it would make my work much easier,' Eppy said. 'But I don't really believe yours is like any of those we've been discussing. I think it's a new type.'

'A good, kindly type?' I asked, to reassure Sean.

'Quite possibly, since it has been helping Sean's family over a long period of time. I've actually been aware that there was one here in Ireland . . .' Then he leaned toward Sean, pointing an arthritically deformed finger at him.

'Is that why you've been rooting around this area for so long?' I asked, for that admission clarified many questions about Epiphanius Tighe.

'Yes,' and Eppy turned to Sean with a very reassuring expression on his face. 'It's probably a monocephalic quadruped and it could or could not be pyropneumonic. Definitely acquisitive. Possibly of a generous disposition since it's paid its rent to your family for the use of the premises . . .' Eppy looked expectantly at Sean, hoping now, I rather suspected, to hear details of the position of the hoard.

Sean rose, however, using both hands to push his hair back.

'I really do appreciate all your help. I'm just unsure if I ought to allow any non-family people into its premises. If you take my point.'

Rather to my surprise, Eppy managed to hide what must have been a terrible disappointment to him.

'Sleep on it then, Sean. But believe that my interest in visiting the site is purely academic, in my role of psycho-taxonomist. Purely academic! But this manifestation is *so* unusual in many regards, that I would take it as a very kind gesture on your part to have, as they say in these parts, a gawk at it.'

'You're most understanding . . .'

'And I'm certain the dragon appreciates your scruples,' Eppy said, nodding and wearing his wisest expression. The old fraud. He was *dying* to see the hoard and eye-ball this dragon. But he was handling Sean like the wily old *Seannachie* that he was.

'It's late anyhow,' I said, rising. 'I can't handle these twenty-hour talk sessions as easily as I once could. Sleep on it, Sean.'

'And if anything . . . *anything* occurs to change the status quo,' Eppy said, 'give us a shout.'

'Yes, indeed, Sean. Do.'

We saw him out and, by the time I had locked the house up, Eppy had retired to his room. I thought of knocking on his door and demanding a few more explanations about Messer Epiphanius Tighe, Psycho-Taxonomist, but I was too tired to summon the energy to deal with Eppy if he didn't wish to volunteer any further information.

Epilogue

I WAS ROUSED from a much-needed sleep by the insistent ring of the phone. I did *not* want to leave my bed but the phone was not going to let up. People don't give up if there is some kind of an emergency. I dragged out of bed to answer it.

'Look, there has been a significant change,' said Sean, his tone urgent.

'You've met the dragon?'

'Not exactly. but I want you to come here! Please? As soon as you can . . .'

'Look, soon as I can may not be soon enough if there's been a drastic change.'

'Ah, but, you see,' and there was a ripple of laughter in his voice. 'I've been codding you a bit. I'm not that far from you there in Wicklow.'

'Oh?'

And he gave me explicit directions. I didn't know whether to fault or compliment him on his discretion.

'It shouldn't take you more than twenty minutes.'

'You don't know how I drive.'

'The faster the better before it all goes away.'

'What? The hoard?' I was anxious now. How many people – still living – have seen a real dragon hoard? I like being first at things – well, I'll settle for second with a dragon's hoard. 'Eppy will be ecstatic.'

'Yes,' Sean replied in a droll fashion, 'I'm sure he will.'

Why was I not surprised to find Epiphanius Tighe standing in the door to the guest room, looking as bright as if he'd slept twenty-four instead of four hours?

'You can't have tapped the phone!'

'I haven't been a psycho-taxonomist as long as I have without recognizing draconic vibrations in the air. He's not so far from here, after all, is our Sean?'

'No, he isn't. Where are you going?'

He had detoured into the kitchen and then into the utility room and was opening cupboards.

'We'll need that emergency lantern of yours,' he said. 'Ah, and the canister is full.' He whooshed me toward my own door.

'Don't dally, woman! I don't want to miss this because you're slow. And I'll need my helmet. Maybe this time . . .' He grabbed the disreputable affair he wore as protection when riding his bike and scrambled into the car.

'I wouldn't miss this for anything,' and I jackrabbited the car into reverse and had the satisfaction of seeing Eppy reach for the 'ojaysus' handle above the door. 'And slow I'm not!'

I made it to Sean's in seventeen minutes, in spite of having to do a complete circle when Eppy suddenly said that I had to take the left-hand road of the fork.

'But the signpost reads . . .'

'Kids! Turning the posts about again,' he said in a growl. 'I know where we're going.'

'Why doesn't that surprise me?'

'Should. I only just figured it out myself,' Eppy had the grace to admit in a somewhat apologetic tone. That mollified me no end. 'Don't miss the drive,' and he stabbed his index finger to the left. 'And watch those potholes . . .'

Just as well Eppy warned me, because the long drive up to the Georgian house looked like a Bosnian minefield, pitted and holed by the torrential rains we've been having. I had to slow down or risk the suspension of the Camry.

'There!' And Eppy's voice rose in the first excitement I've ever heard him utter. '*There*!'

He pointed to a ruined twelfth-century tower which had evidently degenerated into a garden feature: broken off just above the single portal that had once given access to those sheltering in the tower from Viking raids. I was gawking so at that that I nearly ran Sean Evans down as he came running out of the stable block beside the house.

'Hurry!' he said, breathlessly, as he cupped my elbow with his arm and, with the other hand, towed Eppy along, helmet banging his side. We both had to half-run to keep up with Sean's long stride.

He led us back around the stables, down a gravelled path towards the old tower, and then beside the bank that had added to the tower's impregnability. Even Eppy had to duck to pass through the hole in that hill and I knew why he'd been wise to collect a lantern and helmet. A short crouching walk and then we could all straighten up in the hidden chamber.

Then I was dumb struck: the lanterns Sean had placed about the roughly circular space illuminated the most incredible pile of valuable junk I had ever seen. He hadn't been kidding! I had never thought he meant a hoard of *this* size. Touching's believing and Sean shooed us with hand gestures towards the pile. Eppy's chuckle was smug as he held the gas lantern up to appraise the amassed wealth. I still couldn't believe what my eyes were seeing so I stepped up. Oddly enough, Eppy shook his head, almost regretfully, when Sean urged him forward, too.

I could not let this opportunity pass me by, whatever restrained Eppy. Torn between fascination and a healthy regard for known draconic reprisals, I scooped up a handful of coins and gems. A golden gem-incrusted goblet rolled to knock against my toe, its movement loosening several coins which spun down. I picked one up, dribbling the gems back into the mass.

'Oh!' I said. 'Another new one? Or one of those you showed us last night?'

'New,' and Sean slapped his pocket until the bunch inside jingled. 'She, or he, was on the take last night again. But that's not why I phoned you. Wait, and watch. It's about to happen again.' He gestured toward the hoard and suddenly the whole thing seemed to shift. No, to dissipate. 'Did you see that?'

I swallowed and glanced at Eppy. He was startled, too. Sean's dragon was teaching that old know-it-all a new draconic wrinkle, if I didn't mistake my reading of his surprise.

'Some if it – went – elsewhere?' I stepped closer to Sean and then wondered if that was the proper direction. I know too much about dragons to be brave in their vicinity. And yet . . . was this to be my big opportunity? Not only to see its hoard, but – the dragon? I caught a glimpse of Eppy peering into the shadows. But there wasn't room, what with the hoard and us, for anything else in the space available. Though more was becoming available.

'It's been happening every few minutes,' Sean said. 'The mass gets misty and then a layer or so disappears. I even put a casket with gold and ivory inlay on the top to be sure I wasn't mistaken. It disappeared. That's when I called you.'

'You're a lucky lad, Sean,' Eppy remarked wryly. 'Your dragon may be sneaky but at least it's not punitive.'

Another layer was skimmed off, and coins and gems settled into new positions.

'The process is speeding up,' Sean said anxiously.

'Not so much mass to shift,' I said, speaking the thought in my head.

'It *was* much higher,' Sean said, raising his hand to a level above his head. 'D'you believe me?' He wanted us to.

I could only nod for the shimmering had occurred again – not a *Star Trek* beam-me-up-Scotty, but a blurring of the whole so that you weren't really sure it was disappearing, only the level of the hoard was definitely sinking.

Then Sean reached down and grabbed up two handfuls: several thick, heavy chains, some uncut stones, coins, and a gold and begemmed hand-mirror which he stuffed into his pockets.

I thought – briefly – of doing the same but I wasn't family and had no ethical or moral right to touch it. I noticed that Eppy

didn't move so much as an inch closer. Just seeing it was enough of a spectacle for us.

As we watched, mesmerized, the hoard was disappearing at an ever-increasing rate, becoming so rapid a process that the remnants seemed to melt and details of what was left could not be distinguished from the mass. Then, in one interval, a strange object sort of rolled down off the whole pile. With a rapturous exclamation of discovery, Eppy leaped forward and snatched it up.

'It is, it has to be,' he cried, and whipping the helmet off his shoulder, began fiddling with the object on the front of it. I looked more closely and the thing resembled nothing so much as an eye-band, like that Geordie wears in *Star Trek* (which I've been told started life out as a girl's hairband). Only this was wider and heavier than Geordie's appliance. Fascinated I watched as Eppy actually snapped the band across the open space and lifted it up and down like the visor it was!

'My word! How old is that helmet?' I demanded.

Eppy didn't answer, staring at the now complete helmet as if all the Christmases in the world had just dumped their presents on him.

'I've got it.' Eppy was hugging it to his chest, his eyes glowing.

'So has the dragon,' Sean said, pointing.

Suddenly there wasn't a coin or jewel or chain left of the immense hoard that had only moments ago occupied the packed earth floor. Sean protectively clapped his hands to his pockets. By his relieved expression, I knew that his purloined objects were still present. Abruptly the ground started to tremble.

I grabbed Sean's arm and heard Eppy's exclamation of amazement. For the dimensions of the cave had altered.

'Grab the other lantern, Anne,' Sean said as he reached for the one at his side.

'We'd best leave,' Eppy added as if we were witless enough not to realize what was happening.

I fumbled for the lantern and turned as the volume of open space around us was contracting with dizzying speed.

'*Move!*' Sean pulled me about, pushing me after Eppy's disappearing figure and propelling me ahead of him through the access tunnel. We had just time enough to emerge before the aperture closed over completely. I blinked and there was grass covering the slope where the cave entrance had been, grass that looked like it hadn't been touched in centuries. 'My God, we might have been trapped in there.'

Buried alive? By a vengeful dragon? I hadn't heard anything about that sort of behaviour. Dragons tended to flame first, ask after. Eppy calmly turned off the lantern which he handed to me. Then, with the air of someone girding his loins, shifting his Colt in its holster in preparation for action, Eppy put the helmet on his head, the visor bit slapping back against the crown. He took a deep breath, and using his elbows to hitch up his pants, he lifted one hand to slip the visor over his eyes and the other in a farewell wave to us as he strode forward. I watched, speechless. Had he actually assembled, before my very eyes, the Dragon Helm of legend that would allow the user to *see* dragons?

But Sean was slapping at his pockets now and my attention was diverted. I watched, holding my breath, as he lifted one chain out. I could see in the light of the lanterns we held that the other pieces still bulged in his possession.

'She didn't take 'em,' Sean said with great relief.

'Paid you the rent,' I suggested. 'And it's not a vindictive sort.'

'But what sort of dragon *was* it?' he demanded, first of me, and then Eppy.

'I dunno,' I said with a shrug and turned toward Eppy who had reached the lawn on the other side of the tower. 'Is the Dragon Helm what it should be?'

'Oh, definitely,' Eppy said in a crow of triumph.

'Well, if you can see it, what kind is it?' I demanded.

'Not quite sure yet,' he replied, 'but, considering its recent behaviour, it has to be a new manifestation.'

'Fourteen thousand seven hundred and thirty?' I asked facetiously, to cover a rising anxiety.

'I do believe so.'

'Can you *see* it?' I asked, a little apprehensive, remembering his story about the Gwynedd dragon.

He turned towards us in the dim but brightening morning light. 'Tell me now, Sean, Anne, do *you* believe in dragons?'

'I do,' Sean said staunchly.

'I *have* to,' I said for a variety of reasons: the most recent having to do with the size of the hoard I had seen disappearing by means of no known agency.

'Say it!' Eppy cried in a voice that was more intense than loud.

I thought of Tinker Bell. And grabbed hold of Sean's hand. 'I believe. I do. I do! I *do*!' We chorused in unison, his baritone so much more fervent than mine that I increased the volume of my voice.

Suddenly I could see a movement, like a breeze, a sinuous movement against the forsythia bushes on the far side of the lawn where Eppy stood.

'At last, my lovely, my darling, I have you. Take me with you, I implore you. Take me with you!' Eppy cried.

As Sean and I watched with rivetted gaze, Eppy seemed to elevate, his legs assumed a riding position and he was lifted above ground. Eppy let out a cowboy yell that ought to have been heard in Dublin! I clung to Sean then, and he to me. Eppy was clearly a-straddle *something*.

'What kind of dragon is it?' I cried, as he was rising even further above ground, taking off in fact.

'A very special one,' I heard his voice, whipped back over his shoulder, as whatever it was achieved height.

'Eppy, what *kind*?' Surely he'd know by now!

'A female and very pregnant. That's why she's moved her hoard, Sean. She needs more space.' Then he added one more word or phrase. It sounded like 'footsanglung?'

That Chinese dragon he had mentioned very early this morning? He was now too far away for any repetition. And what did it matter? Really! I kept clinging to Sean Evans. And he to me as we watched Eppy's slight figure disappearing in the distance.

'Well, if it was just more space she needed . . .' Sean began with deep regret and sighed. 'It's been rather . . . reassuring . . . to know this old place had . . .' and he grinned, 'intrinsic value.'

'Definitely intrinsic. And neat about packing up, wasn't she? More's the pity.'

'More would have been greedy,' Sean said, feeling his left pocket. I could feel that the contents in the right one were still very much present.

'And you've had the distinct privilege of having a benign and caring family dragon.'

Sean nodded slowly. 'I've had that and I'll remember her.'

We could barely make out Eppy's figure now.

Maybe it was the clouds scudding in the high winds which are always over Ireland. But, for just a scant moment, orange-gold against that clear bright sky, I could have sworn I, too, saw the shape of wings, vast in their spread: and between them, slender and graceful, what could have been a long sinuous body and tail.

'I believe in dragons,' I said softly and Sean nodded affirmation. 'I do. I do. I do.'

NOTES

1   Barbara Hambly, *Dragonsbane*, 1986. pp. 197–201.

2   Kenneth Grahame, *The Reluctant Dragon*, 1930. pp. 106–146.

3   Terry Pratchett, *Guards! Guards*, 1989. p. 132 and 270.

4   Robin McKinley, *The Hero and the Crown*, 1985. pp. 79–81.

5   Gordon R. Dickson, *The Dragon and the George*, 1976. pp. 20–21.

6   Ibid. pp. 172–174.

7   Melanie Rawn, *The Dragon Token*, 1992. pp. 411–413.

8   Jane Yolen, *Dragon's Blood*, 1982. pp. 208–218.

9   Andre Norton and Mercedes Lackey, *The Elevenbane*, 1991. pp. 17–21.

10   Ursula K. Le Guin, 'Orm Embary' from *The Farthest Shore*, 1971.
    pp. 100–107.

11   Anne McCaffrey, *Dragonflight*, 1969. pp. 60–61.

OTHER SOURCES

'The story of Fraich', adapted from J F. Campbell, *The Celtic Dragon Myth*,
T. Grant, Edinburgh, 1911.

'Little Rolling-pea', adapted from *Sixty Folk-tales* from Exclusively Slavonic
Sources, trans. by A. H. Wratislaw, [Eliot Stock, London, 1889], reprinted,
Arno Press, New York, 1977, pp. 132–38.

The Story of Lludd and Llewelys, adapted from *The Mabinogi*[on], ed. and
trans. by Lady Charlotte Guest, Bernard Quartich, London, 1877.

'The Story of Beowulf', freely adapted from Roger Lancelyn Green, *A Book of
Dragons*, illustrated by Krystyna Turska, Harmondsworth, Middlesex: Puffin
Books, 1974, and other sources.

'The Story of Rustem', ibid.

'The Story of Lancelot', ibid.

'The Tale of Melusine', freely adapted from Katherine Briggs, *An Encyclopedia
of Fairies, Hobgoblins, Brownies, Bogies and other Supernatural Creatures*,
Pantheon, New York, n, 1976, pp. 285–87, and other sources.

Joseph Fontenrose, *Python: A study of Delphic Myth and Its Origins*, Berkerley
and London, University of California Press, 1980.

Ernest Ingersoll, *Dragons and Dragon Lore* (1928), Singing Tree Press, Detroit,
1968.

G. Elliot Smith, *The Evolution of the Dragon*, Manchester University Press,
Manchester, 1919.

CLASSIFICATIONS OF DRAGONS

This section enables the reader to cross-reference specific dragon-types with books which deal with these characteristics.

Numbers set in 'superior' character relate to the numbered bibliography which follows.

DRACONIC SIZE

Big to Huge	Medium	Small	Known Fire–Breathers	Hoarders
Griaule[9]	Keman[2]	Wyvern[49]	Nargri[29]	Smaug[21]
Kookluk[50]	Alara[2]	Errol[3]	Glory Road Dragon[19]	Morkeleb[1]
Morkeleb[1]	Pratchett Dragon[3]	Secoh[5]	Morkeleb[1]	Rawn Dragons[6]
Ramoth[4]	Ruth[4]	Mayland Long[7]	Pernese dragons[4]	Unlikely Ones[35]
Chou-Lin[40]	Cook Dragons[26]	fire-lizards[4]	Stegoman[44]	Sybel[37]
Darknight[47]	Heart's Blood[10]	Pip[11]	Heart's Blood[10]	The Kin[2]
Jet aka Nightwing[46]	Bottle O'Rum[10]	Silbakor[12]	Bottle O'Rum[10]	Gyld[37]
Taivimbra[42]	Duane Dragon[13]	Nargry[29]	Errol[4]	Ymareth[15]
Wheviron[42]	Freisner Dragon[27]	Horace[25]	Draconis nobilis[4]	Kazul[16]
Smaug[21]	Glory Road Dragon[17]	Gleep[64]	Chaffinch[32]	Hasai' sVheress[13]
Turiana[46]	Pernese Bronze & Brown Pernese		Rawn dragons[6]	Blanpied Dragons[38]
Vermithrax[55]	Myrenateli[2]	blue	Zatanas' Dragons[25]	Amalek[80]
Father Dragon[2]	Rovytern[2]	& green	Gleep[64]	Freisner[27]
Mnementh[4]	Rauglothor[78]		Vermithrax[55]	Dalvenjah[51]
Gorbash[5]	Blanpied Dragons[38]		Kulculcan[18]	
Smrgol[5]	Anderson[81]		Grizel[18]	
Azhdeen[6]	Sleeth[23]		Grimley[18]	
Elisel[6]	Freisner[27]		Grippeldice[18]	
Elidi[6]			Gyld[37]	
Duncan's[49]			Hasai s'Vheress[13]★	
Belaparthalion[49]			Ruaglothgor[78]★	
Chaffinch[32]			Rosa[38]	
Ymareth[15]			Vlad[38]	
Ember[47]			Orm Embar[14]	
Kazul[16]			Kalessin[14]	
Lady Scarsnout[75]			P Anderson's[81]	
Hasai s'Vheress etc.[13]			Dalvenjah[51]	
Rauglothgor[78]			Sleeth[28]	
Vlad[38]			Freisner's[27]	
Rosa[38]				
Falkor[79]				
Amalek[80]				
Orm Embar[14]				
Kalessin[14]				
Snow Dragon[84]				
Fingard[57]				
Ti Lung[57]				
Aldagon[82]				
Dalvenjah[57]				

★ *Means of Destruction: Anderson dragon, by water. Freisner, by shield and sword, respectively.*

★ And lots more that didn't have names or weren't given approximate categories of size.

Nice Guys		Bad Guys	Shape-Changers
The Kin[2]	Secoh[5]	Jet aka Nightwing[46]	The Dawn Treader[19]
Pernese Dragons[4]	Hubert[60]	Winter[45]	Ged[14]
Swamp Dragon[3]	Taivimbra[42]	Vorgulremik[51]	Tehanu[14]
Horace[25]	Wheviros[42]	Termagant[52]	Ymareth[15]
Yorba of Erianne[31]	Turiana[46]	Long Horned	Wyrd[33]
	Mayland Long[7]	Murderer[52]	Chou-Lin[40]
Faf[33]	Seastrider[72]	Striding Murderer[52]	Thong[40]
Quench Fire[24]	Kulkulcan[18]	Fiend[52]	Sweetness[43]
Wrede Dragon[16]	Grimley[18]	Jugger[52]	Taivimbra[42]
Heart's Blood[10]	Grizel[18]	Bottle O'Rum[10]	Wheviros[42]
Azhdeen[6]	Grippeldice[18]	Blue Horror[52]	Alara[2]
Elisel[6]	Stegoman[44]	Gairoth[63]	Keman[2]
Elidi[6]	Hasais' Vheress[13]	Strabo[65]	Father Dragon[2]
Gorbash[5]	Falkor[38]	Zenphos[26]	Winter[45]
Ymareth[15]	Kalessin[14]	Chaffinch[32]	Changelings[22]
Nyct[33]	Orm Embar[14]	Wyvern[49]	Belaparthalion[49]
Soladon[33]	Snow Dragon[84]	Rahastava[48]	Mayland Long[7]
Myst[33]	Fingard[57]	Vermithrax[55]	Blanpied Dragons[38]*
Dalvenjah[51]	Ti Lung[57]	Chou-Li[40]	Freisner[27]†
Rognoth[63]	Aldagon[82]	Thong[40]	Jenny Waynest[1]‡
Yochi-San[24]	Dalvenjah[51]	Dragons Three[61]	Esmeralda[73]‡
Kookluk[50]		Baalan[46]	Shanzie[57]‡
Belaparthalion[49]	*Undecided: Pyramid Thirteen[29b],*	Chrysophylax[21]	
Ebony[33]	*Vicia-Heinox[28], Gyld[37].*	Glaurung[21]	
		Ember[47]	
		Xanth Dragons[25]	
		Rovytern[2]	
		Myrenateli[2]	
		Rauglothor[78]	
		Blanpied dragons[38]	
		Anderson[81]	
		Sleeth[23]	
		Freisner[27]	

*In that they can become invisible
at their discretion,
'miming' their background.
†enlarging.
‡or shape-changing.*

ANNOTATIONS, REFERRING TO DRACONIC ESOTERICA

1. *Dragonsbane*, Barbara Hambly. Ballantine/Del Rey, 1986.
2. *The Elvenbane*, Andre Norton & Mercedes Lackey. Ballantine/Del Rey, 1991.
3. *Guards! Guards!*, Terry Pratchet. Corgi ed. 1989.
4. *Dragonflight*, Anne McCaffrey. Ballantine, 1969.
   Dragonquest, Ballantine, 1971.
   Dragonsong, Atheneum Publishers, 1976.
   Dragonsinger, Atheneum Publishers, 1977.
   The White Dragon, Del Rey, 1978.
   Dragondrums, Atheneum Publishers, 1979.
   Moreta, Dragonlady of Pern, Del Rey, 1985.
   Nerilka's Story, Del Rey, 1986.
   Dragonsdawn, Del Rey, 1989.
   Renegades of Pern, Del Rey, 1990.
   All the Weyrs of Pern, Del Rey, 1991.
5. *The Dragon and the George*, Gordon R Dickson. Ballantine/Del Rey, 1976.
   The Dragon Knight, Ballantine/Del Rey, 1990.
6. *The Dragon Prince*, Melanie Rawn. Daw Books, 1988.
   The Star Scroll, Daw Books, 1989.
   Sunrunner's Fire, Daw Books, 1990.
   Stronghold, Daw Books, 1991.
   The Dragon Token, Daw Books, 1992.
7. *Tea with the Black Dragon*, R A McAvoy. Bantam, 1983.
8. *Perilous Seas*, Dave Duncan. Del Rey, 1990.
9. *The Man Who Painted Griaule*, Lucius Shepherd. Mark Zeising, 1984.
   The Scalehunter's Beautiful Daughter, Mark Zeising, 1988.
10. *Dragon's Blood*, Jane Yolen. Futura, 1982.
11. *For Love of Mother Not*, Alan Dean Foster. Del Rey, 1983.
12. *Dragonsword*, Gael Baudino. Lynx Omega Books, 1988.
13. *So You Wanna be a Wizard*, Diane Duane. Bantam, 1983.
    Door into Shadow, Bantam, 1984.
14. *Wizard of Earthsea Trilogy*, Ursula K. Le Guin. Parnassus Press, 1968.
    Tehanu, Penguin, 1992.
15. *The Dragon Lord*, Peter Morwood. Daw Books, 1986.
16. *Dealing With Dragons*, Patricia Wrede. Harcourt Brace Jovanovich, 1990.
17. *Glory Road*, Robert A Heinlein. Ballantine, 1966.

18. *Song of Sorcery*, Elizabeth Ann Scarborough. Bantam, 1982.
    The Drastic Dragon of Draco, Texas, Bantam, 1986.
    The Unicorn Creed, Bantam, 1983.
    The Christening Quest, Bantam, 1985.
19. *The Voyage of the Dawn Treader*, C S Lewis. Macmillan, 1952.
20. *The Hero and the Crown*, Robin McKinley. Greenwillow, 1985, Berkley Books, 1986.
21. *The Hobbit*, J R R Tolkien. Houghton Mifflin, 1937, Ballantine, 1965.
    Farmer Giles of Ham, Allen & Unwin, 1949.
    The Silmarillion, Ballantine, 1979.
22. *Once Upon a Time*, ed. Lester del Rey. Del Rey Books, 1991.
23. *Dragonsdoom*, Dennis McKieran. Bantam/Spectra, 1990.
24. *The Gentle Dragon*, Joseph Coates. Lane & Assoc., 1979.
25. *Xanth Series*, Piers Anthony:
    Dragon on a Pedastal, Ballantine/Del Rey, 1983.
    Crewel Lye, Ballantine/Del Rey, 1985.
    Heaven Sent, Avon Books, 1989.
26. *Wizard War Chronicles*, Hugh Cook. Popular Library/Questar, 1987.
27. *New York by Knight*, Esther Freisner. NAL/Signet, 1986.
28. *The Prophet of Lamath*, Robert Don Hughes. Ballantine, 1979.
    The Forging of the Dragon, Ballantine, 1989.
29. *Sword Smith*, Eleanor Arnason. Condor Publishing, 1978.
    Daughter of the Bear King, Avon Books, 1987.
30. *Dragon's Gold*, Piers Anthony & Robert Margroff. Tor, 1987.
31. *The Magicians of Erianne*, James R Berry. Harper & Row, 1988.
32. *Doomfarers of Coromande*, Brian Daley. Ballantine/Del Rey, 1977.
33. *Dragon's Pawn*, Carol L. Dennis. Questar, 1987.
    Dragon's Knight, Questar, 1989.
34. *Dragon's Milk*, Susan Fletcher. Atheneum, 1989.
35. *The Unlikely Ones*, Mary Brown. McGraw Hill, 1986, Baen Books, 1987.
36. *The Sea Hag*, David Drake. Baen Books, 1988.
37. *The Forgotten Beasts of Eld*, Patricia McKillip. Atheneum Publishers, 1975.
38. *Dragons: An Introduction to the Modern Infestation*, Pamela Wharton Blanpied. Warner, 1980.
39. *The Fairy of Ku–She*, Lucie M Chin. Ace Books, 1988.

40. *Web of Defeat*, Lionel Fenn. Tor Books, 1987.
41. *Blue Moon Rising*, Simon Green. NAL/Roc, 1991.
42. *Giftwish*, Graham D Martin. Houghton Mifflin, 1981.
    Catchfire, Houghton Mifflin, 1982.
43. *Mage–Born Child*, Jonathan Wylie. Bantam/Spectra, 1988.
44. *Her Majesty's Wizard*, Christopher Stasheff. Ballantine/Del Rey, 1986.
45. *The Floating Dragon*, Peter Straub. Putnam, 1983,
    Berkley, 1984.
46. *Where Dragons Lie*, R A Salsitz. NAL/Signet, 1985.
    Where Dragons Rule, Signet, 1986.
    Night of the Dragons, Signet, 1990.
47. *Stormblade*, Nancy Berberick. TSR Inc., 1988.
48. *The Dragon Lord*, David Drake. Berkley/Putnam, 1979,
    Tor Books, 1982.
    The Sea Hag, Baen Books, 1988.
49. *The Secret Country Trilogy*, Pamela Dean. Ace Books, 1985.
    The Hidden Land, Ace Books, 1986.
    The Whim of the Dragon, Ace Books, 1989.
50. *The Curse of Sagamore*, Kara Dalkey. Ace Books, 1986.
51. *Make Way for Dragons*, Thorarinn Gunnarson. Ace Books, 1990.
    Humans, Beware!, Ace Books, 1990.
52. *The Dragon Masters*, Jack Vance. Galaxy Publishing, 1962.
53. *Shadowrun: Never Deal with a Dragon*, Robert A Charrette. NAL/Roc, 1990.
54. *Dragon's Bane*, *The Wiz Zumwalt* Series, Rick Cook. Baen Books, 1989.
    Wizardry Compiled, Baen Books, 1990.
    Wizardry Cursed, Baen Books, 1991.
55. *Dragonslayer*, Wayland Drew. Ballantine/Del Rey, 1981.
56. *Chess with a Dragon*, David Gerrold. Walker & Co., 1987.
57. *A Voice for Princess*, John Morrissey. Ace Books, 1986.
    The Questing of Kedrigern Ace Books, 1987.
    Kedrigern in Wanderland Ace Books, 1988.
58. *Magicians of Erianne*, James R Berry. Harper & Row, 1988.
59. *Harlot's Ruse*, Esther Freisner. Questar, 1986.
60. *The Ebenezum & the Ballad of Wuntvor* Series, Craig Shaw Gardner.
    A Malady of Magics, Ace Books, 1986.
61. *Dragon Fall*, Lee J Hindle. Avon/Flare, 1984.

62. *The Spellsinger* Series, Alan Dean Foster. Ballantine Del Rey, 1972.
63. *Gamearth* Trilogy, Kevin J Anderson. NAL/Signet, 1989.
64. *Another Fine Myth*, Robert Aspirin. Donning/Starblaze, 1978.
65. *Magic Kingdom for Sale*, Terry Brooks. Ballantine/Del Rey, 1986.
66. *The Terra Magica* Series, Lin Carter. Daw Books, 1982.
67. *The Incorporated Knight*, L Sprague de Camp, Catherine Cook.
    Phantasia Press, 1987.
68. *Calabrinia Falling*, Pilar de Ovalle. Crossing Press, 1990.
69. *The Flight of the Dragon*, Peter Dickinson. Harper & Row, 1979.
70. *The Eyes of the Dragon*, Stephen King. Viking, 1987.
71. *The Dragon's Hoard*, Tanith Lee. Farrar, Straus Girous, 1971.
72. *Nightpool*, Shirley R Murphy. Harper & Row, 1985.
    The Ivory Lyre, Harper & Row, 1987.
    The Dragonbards, Harper & Row, 1988.
73. *A Baroque Fable*, Chelsea Quinn Yarbro. Berkley, 1986.
74. *Dragonlover's Guide to Pern*, Jody–Lynn Nye. Del Rey, 1989.
75. *Elric of Melnibone*, Michael Moorcock:
    The Revenge of the Rose, BCA, Grfton, 1991.
76. *Dragonworld*, Byron Preiss and Michael Reaves. Bantam, 1983.
77. *The Shattered World*, Michael Reaves. Timescape, 1984.
78. *Spellfire*, ed. Greenwood. TSR, Inc., 1987.
79. *The Neverending Story*, Michael Ende. Doubleday, 1983.
80. *A Forest Lord*, Michael Williams. Warner/Questar, 1991.
81. *Three Hearts and Three Lions*, Paul Anderson. Doubleday, 1961.
82. *Blood of a Dragon*, Lawrence Watt–Evans. Del Rey, 1991.
83. *A Horsewoman in Godsland*, Claudia J Edwards. Popular Library, 1987.
84. *The Fallen Country*, Somtow Sucharitkul, Bantam, 1986.
85. *Dragon Season*, Michael Cassutt. Tor, 1991.
86. *Dragonbound*, Carl Miller. Ace Books, 1988.

Additional books examined but not annotated:

In Between Dragons, Michael Kandel. Bantam/Spectra, 1990.
The Sword and the Chain, Joel Rosenberg. Grafton UK, 1988.
Ice Dragon, Richard A Knaak. Orbit UK, 1989.
Dragon Magic, Andre Norton. Ace Books, 1973.
Peregrinus Primus, Avram Davidson. Ace Books, 1971.
    Rogue Dragon, Ace Books, 1965.

DRAGON BOOKS AND ESOTERIC LISTS THEREOF

Books about Dragons by Modern Authors (alphabetical)

ANDERSON, Kevin J. Games End
ANDERSON, Paul. Three Hearts and Three Lions
ANTHONY, Piers. Dragon on a Pedestal
ANTHONY, Heaven Sent
ANTHONY, Piers and MARGROFF, Robert E.
  Dragon's Gold
ANTHONY, Orc's Opal
ARNASON, Eleanor. Daughter of the Bear King
ARNASON, The Sword Smith
ASIMOV, Isaac and editors. Dragon Tales
ASPIRIN, Robert. Another Fine Myth
BAUDINO, Gael. Dragonsword
BERBERICK, Nancy Varian. Stormblade
BERRY, James R. Magicians of Erianne
BETANCOURT, John G. Rogue Pirate
BLANPIED, Pamela W. Dragons:
  An Introduction to the Modern Infestation
BRODERICK, Damien. The Dreaming Dragons
BROOKS, Terry. Magic Kingdom For Sale
BROUN, Heywood. The Fifty–First Dragon
BROWN, Mary. The Unlikely Ones
CARD, Orson Scott ed. Dragons of Light
CARD, Dragons of Darkness
CARTER, Lin. Kesrick
CARTER, Dragonrouge
CASSUTT, Michael. Dragon Season
CHARRETTE, Robert N. Shadowrun One
CHARRETTE, Shadowrun Two
CHIN, M Lucie. The Fairy of Ku–She
COATES, Joseph K. The Gentle Dragon
COOK, Hugh. Wizard War
COOK, Rick. Wizard's Bane
COOK, Wizardry Compiled
COOK, Wizardry Cursed
DALEY, Brian. Doomfarers of Coramonde
DALKEY, Kara. The Curse of Sagamor
DAVIDSON, Avram. Rogue Dragon
DE CAMP, L Sprague and COOK, Catherine.
  The Incorporate Knight
DE OVALLE, Pilar. Calabrinia Falling
DEAN, Pamela. The Whim of the Dragon
DENNIS, Carol L. Dragon's Pawn
DENNIS, Dragon's Knight
DICKINSON, Peter. Flight of Dragons
DICKSON, Gordon R. The Dragon and the George
DICKSON, The Dragon Knight
DRAKE, David. The World of Crystal Walls
DREW, Wayland. Dragonslayer
DUANE, Diane. So you Wanna Be a Wizard
DUANE, Door into Shadow

DUNCAN, Dave. Perilous Seas,
  in 'A Man of his Word'
EDWARDS, Claudia J A. Horsewoman in Godsland
FENN, Lionel. Blood River Down
FLETCHER, Susan. Dragon's Milk
FOSTER, Alan Dean. For Love of Mother–Not
FOSTER, Spellsinger
FREISNER, Esther M. Harlot's Ruse
FREISNER, New York by Knight
GARDNER, Craig Shaw. A Malady of Magicks
GERROLD, David. Chess with a Dragon
GRAHAME, Kenneth. The Reluctant Dragon
GRANT, Katheryn. The Land of Ten Thousand
  Willows
GREEN, Simon R. Blue Moon Rising
HAMBLY, Barbara. Dragonsbane
HEINLEIN, Robert. Glory Road
HINDLE, Lee J. Dragon Fall
HOKE, Helen. Dragons, Dragons, Dragons
HUGHES, Robert D. The Propet of Lamath
LEE, Tanith. The Dragon's Hoard
LE GUIN, Ursula K. The Earthsea Trilogy
  and Tehanu
LEWIS, C S. Voyage of the Dawn Treader
LORD, Jeffrey. Ice Dragon
LORD, The Dragons of Englor
MARTIN, Graham D. Giftwish
MARTIN, Catchfire
McAVOY, R A. Tea with a Black Dragon
McKIERNAN, Dennis. Dragonsdoom
McCAFFREY, Anne. Dragonflight
McCAFFREY, Dragonquest
McCAFFREY, The White Dragon
McCAFFREY, Dragonsong
McCAFFREY, Dragonsinger
McCAFFREY, Dragondrums
McCAFFREY, Moreta, Dragonlady of Pern
McCAFFREY, Dragonsdawn
McCAFFREY, Renegades of Pern
McCAFFREY, All the Weyrs of Pern
McKILLIP, Patricia. The Forgotten Beasts of Eld
McKINLEY, Robin. The Hero and the Crown
MILLER, Carl. Dragonbound
MILLS, Craig. The Bane of Lord Caladon
MOORCOCK, Michael. The Revenge of the Rose
MORRESSY, John. A Voice for Princess
MORRESSY, The Questing of Kedrigern
MORRESSY, Kedrigern in Wonderland
MORWOOD, Peter. The Dragon Lord

MORWOOD, The Horse Lord
MURPHY, Shirley R. Nightpool
MURPHY, The Ivory Lyre
MURPHY, The Dragonbards
NESBIT, E. The Book of Dragons (juv.)
NORTON, Andre. Dragon Magic
NORTON, Andre and LACKEY, Mercedes.
  The Elvenbane
NYE, Jodyn–Lynn. Dragon Lover's Guide
  to Pern
PRATCHETT, Terry. Guards! Guards!
RAWN, Melanie. The Dragon Prince
RAWN, The Star Scrolls
RAWN, Sunrunner's Fire
RAWN, Stronghold
RAWN, The Dragon Token
REAVES–PREISS, Dragonworld
REAVES, Michael. The Shattered World
ROSENBERG, Joel. The Sleeping Dragon
SALSITZ, R A V. Where Dragons Lie
SALSITZ, Where Dragons Rule
SALSITZ, Night of Dragons
SCARBOROUGH, Elizabeth. Song of Sorcery
SCARBOROUGH, The Unicorn Creed
SCARBOROUGH, The Christening Quest
SCARBOROUGH, The Drastic Dragon
  of Draco, TX
SHEPARD, Lucius. Scalehunter's
  Beautiful Daughter
SHEPARD, The Man Who Painted
  the Dragon Griaule
SKY, Kathleen. Witchdame
SMEDS, Dave. The Sorcery Within
STASHEFF, Christopher. Her Majesty's Wizard
STRAUB, Peter. Floating Dragon
SUCHARITKUL, Somtow. The Fallen Country
TOLKIEN, J R R. The Hobbit
TOLKIEN, Farmer Giles of Ham
TOLKIEN, The Silmarillion
VANCE, Jack. Dragon Masters
WATT–EVANS, Lawrence. With a Single Spell
WATT–EVANS, Blood of a Dragon
WEISS–HICKMAN, Dragonlance Series
WREDE, Patricia. Dealing with Dragons
WREDE, Talking with Dragons
WYLIE, Jonathan. The Mage–Born Child
YARBRO, Chelsea Quinn. A Baroque Fable
YOLEN, Jane. Dragon's Blood
ZELAZNY, Roger. Roadmarks

ACKNOWLEDGEMENTS

The publishers would like to thank the following authors, author's agents, publishers and Trusts for permission to reproduce excerpts from their books: the estate of Kenneth Graham, Curtis Brown, London; Terry Pratchett; Robin McKinley, Greenwillow Books, W. M. Morrow & Co; Gordon R. Dickson, The Pimlico Agency, Ralph M. Vicinanza; Melanie Rawn, Daw Books; New York; Jane Yolen, Harcourt Brace & Co; Andre Norton and Mercedes Lackey, Scovil Chichak Galen Literary Agency, Inc., New York; The Ursula K. Le Guin Trust, Virginia Kidd Agency, Inc.

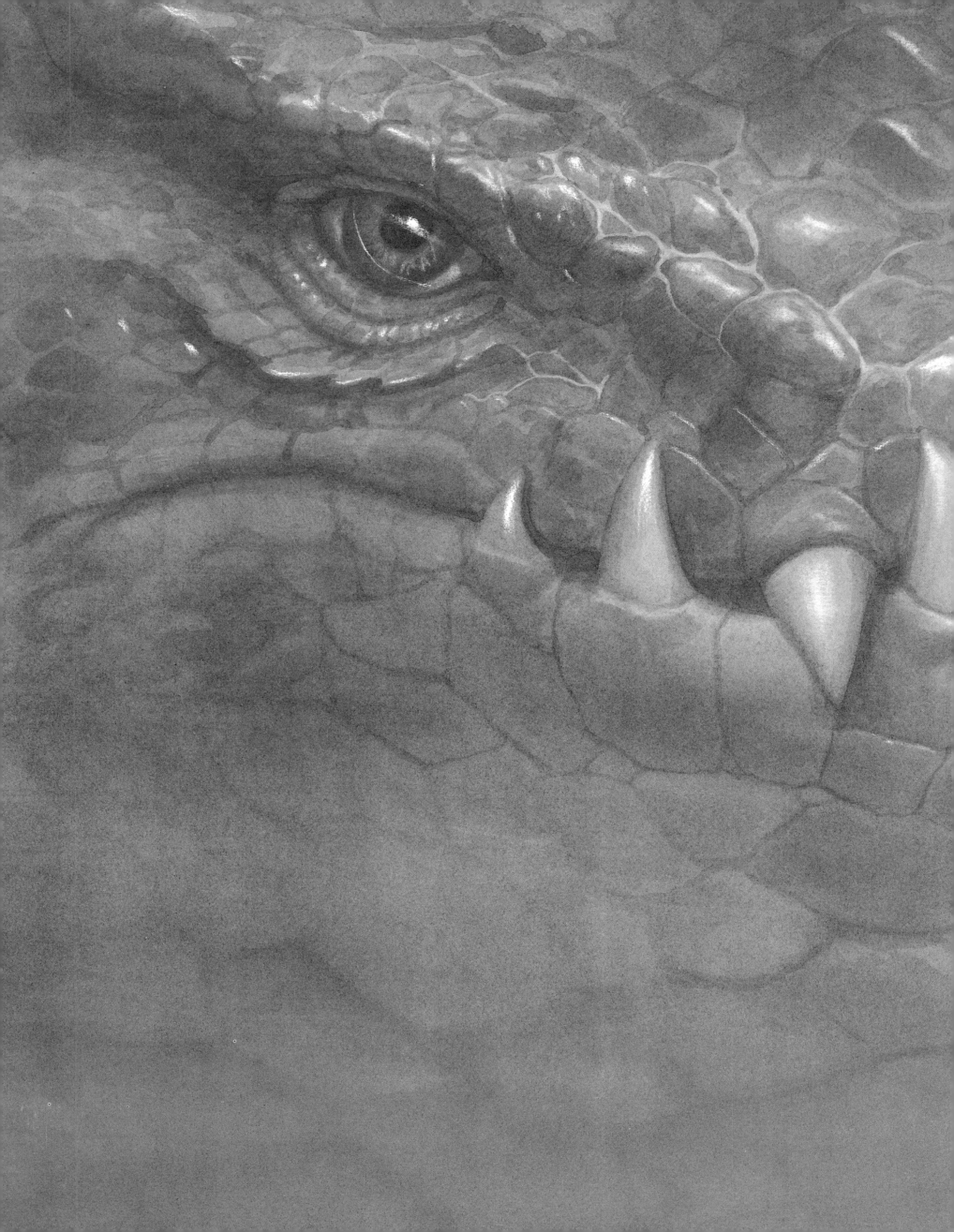